G000293144

YEAR GROUP PHOTOCOPIABLES

YEAR

Paul and Jean Noble

CREDITS

Authors
Paul and Jean Noble

Editor
Roanne Davis

Assistant Editor
Dulcie Booth

Series Designer
Lynne Joesbury

Designer
Paul Cheshire

Illustrations
Ann Kronheimer

Cover photographs
Manipulated images © PHOTODISC (globe, dice, magnet, paint brush, disk),
© DIGITAL VISION (hand), © STOCKBYTE (mask).

Published by Scholastic Ltd,
Villiers House,
Clarendon Avenue,
Leamington Spa,
Warwickshire
CV32 5PR
Printed by Bell & Bain Ltd, Glasgow
Text © 2003 Paul and Jean Noble
© 2003 Scholastic Ltd
1 2 3 4 5 6 7 8 9 0   3 4 5 6 7 8 9 0 1 2

Visit our website at www.scholastic.co.uk

British Library Cataloguing-in-Publication Data
A catalogue record for this book is available from
the British Library.

ISBN 0-439-98301-0

The rights of Paul and Jean Noble to be identified as the Authors of this work has been asserted by them in accordance with the Copyright, Designs and Patents Act 1988.

All rights reserved. This book is sold subject to the condition that it shall not, by way of trade or otherwise, be lent, hired out or otherwise circulated without the publisher's prior consent in any form of binding or cover other than that in which it is published and without a similar condition, including this condition, being imposed upon the subsequent purchaser.

No part of this publication may be reproduced, stored in a retrieval system, or transmitted, in any form or by any means, electronic, mechanical, photocopying, recording or otherwise, without the prior permission of the publisher. This book remains copyright, although permission is granted to copy those pages marked 'photocopiable' for classroom distribution and use only in the school which has purchased the book or by the teacher who has purchased the book and in accordance with the CLA licensing agreement. Photocopying permission is given for purchasers only and not for borrowers of books from any lending service.

Every effort has been made to ensure that websites and addresses referred to in this book are correct and educationally sound. They are believed to be correct at the time of publication. The publishers cannot be held responsible for subsequent changes in the address of a website, nor for the content of the sites mentioned. Referral to a website is not an endorsement by the publisher of that site.

Material from the National Curriculum © Crown copyright. Reproduced with permission of the Controller of HMSO and the Queen's Printer for Scotland. Material from Programmes of Study in the National Curriculum © Qualifications and Curriculum Authority. Reproduced under the terms of HMSO Guidance Note 8. Material from the National Literacy Strategy *Framework for Teaching* and the National Numeracy Strategy *Framework for Teaching Mathematics* © Crown copyright. Reproduced under the terms of the HMSO Guidance Note 8.

CONTENTS

INTRODUCTION

Of all the teaching aids produced in the last 50 years, it is perhaps the worksheet that has proved to be the most useful, the most flexible, the easiest to use, the cheapest, and often the most effective. With improving technology improving its quality, it also looks set to be the most enduring. But worksheets, like teachers, do not operate in a vacuum, for learning is a complex process that only works if there is intellectual activity. The learner's brain has to be switched on. It may be that when a teacher walks into a classroom, brains automatically go on line and it may also be that when one of the photocopiable sheets in this book is handed out, intellectual activity is immediately stimulated. But we doubt it, although we would like to think that it happens sometimes.

This book offers considerable support to teachers working under many pressures, not least that of time constraint, but none of its contents will do the teaching for you. You still have to engage the learner's mind, stimulate interest in the subject and, more often than not, set the context for the work. That said, we are sure that you will find much to help you here and plenty that will challenge, amuse and satisfy your children. The *Year Group Photocopiables* series draws on substantial teaching experience and provides a readily accessible classroom support that can be particularly useful when you are limited by time or challenged by voracious learners. Supply teachers and others 'caught on the hop' will also be able to rely on this material to help them to cope with demanding days.

Teaching Year 3

Year 3 children are sometimes seen as children in transit, going through a fairly substantial phase of physical change whilst moving from infants to juniors; a move that, for some, is also a physical/geographical one. There is still a cultural difference between 'junior' schooling and 'infant' schooling and although the National Curriculum may now make this change a nearly seamless one, it is still a year of change. Many teachers have observed how different a Year 3 class is in January from how it was in September when the year began.

Children in this year face the whole range of curriculum subjects, as they did in Year 2, but with the content of subjects more precisely defined. Devising supportive material such as these photocopiable sheets is a little more problematic where there are choices to be made, as it is obvious that not everyone will choose to teach the same thing. However, learning for Year 3 children, particularly within the Literacy and Numeracy Strategies, is laid down in considerable detail. For other guidance on the choice of content, we have been able to lean heavily upon the schemes of work drawn up by the Qualifications and Curriculum Authority, schemes that are used as the basis for many school syllabuses. (Refer to www.qca.org.uk or www.standards.dfee.gov.uk/schemes.)

What the photocopiable sheets cover

This particular volume is based upon the range of curriculum subjects and experiences that are described within *The National Curriculum: Handbook for primary teachers in England* (www.nc.uk.net). Inevitably, weighting has been given to the core subjects (English, mathematics and science) and the worksheets have been compiled bearing in mind the demands of the Literacy and Numeracy Strategies as well as QCA subject guidance. The non-core foundation subjects (design and technology, information and communication technology, history, geography, art and design and music, with the exception of physical education) are included, but in varying degrees depending upon the suitability of the content to the photocopiable worksheet format. Non-foundation subjects such as religious education and PSHE and citizenship are also covered as far as subject matter allows. The photocopiable sheets do not, of course, cover everything detailed in the National Curriculum and its accompanying documents, nor everything in your school syllabuses, so they cannot constitute a complete curriculum. Rather like basic car insurance, the cover provided here is fundamental rather than comprehensive; a book that attempted to be so would be many times larger than this, as well as being difficult to justify in principle. Nobody wants children to overdose on worksheets.

The choice of photocopiable sheets was made on the following grounds:
● Content and activities must translate sensibly into the photocopiable format. (Activities that are predominantly 'hands-on', colour dependent or oral have been largely avoided.)
● Activities must be worthwhile (in that they contribute towards achieving specific learning objectives) and interesting for the children.
● Subject matter should relate directly to the prescribed National Curriculum.
● Content should satisfy the demands of the Numeracy and Literacy Strategies where possible.

We have largely avoided repetition of sheets in favour of range of cover and in order to keep the book to a manageable size. However, suggestions for reinforcement and extension are included in the teacher's notes.

Using the material

Before using one of the photocopiable sheets, it is recommended that you read the teacher's notes that accompany it. These have deliberately been kept brief and contain four sections:

Objective

This states the learning objective(s) for each sheet. Every objective is linked to the curriculum guidance issued by the government – in English and mathematics, for example, the objectives match targets specified in the Numeracy and Literacy Strategies. Objectives have been stated in direct and non-pretentious terms. However, it is not claimed that children completing a particular sheet will therefore fully achieve that objective – we wish that teaching and learning were that easy.

What to do

This section provides suggestions on how the activity should be introduced and worked through with the children. These instructions repeatedly refer to the adult support that children will require and to the importance of talk and discussion. It is very important to get Year 3 children to 'think out loud' as an aid to learning, but we also expect that they will be given oral instruction and support. Instructions given on the sheets are kept brief, although many children will now have reached a sufficient level of reading competency to cope with quite complex written instructions. Sometimes the worksheet text serves as a memory jogger to the teacher rather than as instruction to the child. The teacher's notes state when, and what, equipment will be required (usually very little), how the activity might be taught (whole class, group, individual instruction) and the degree of adult support that is likely to be needed.

Differentiation

Often, all that is needed to give all the children in the group access to a particular activity is a change in the extent of the attention and instruction given. More confident children will be able to proceed with the minimum of instruction; less able children may need adult support throughout an activity. It is rarely the case that an entirely different activity will be needed to differentiate in order for an objective to be achieved, but if the activity is too difficult for some, you might reconsider setting it for those children at all: if there is a marked mismatch between ability and task, reject the task. (Perhaps a suitable activity will be found in an earlier volume of this series.) The differentiation suggestions in the teacher's notes will point you in the direction of the most accessible modifications.

Extension

These activities can be used as a form of differentiation for more able children, but they are mainly intended to provide some form of reinforcement to help achieve the objective. Apart from where particular apparatus or teaching is required, most of the extension activities could be completed at home. It is recommended that the issues being dealt with (including the support provided for parents), the value of the work at home and competing demands on the child are all considered before homework is set. If you need further extension work, or more differentiation for confident children, you could consult companion volumes in this series.

Progression

Within the subjects, the order of the photocopiable sheets has been kept as logical as possible – the activity on sheet one would usually be expected to be taught before sheet ten, for example. However, the order will not necessarily match the order of your teaching programme and in some subject areas there is simply no obvious order for the teaching of particular activities. Nevertheless, a thread of progression runs through the book, and, more visibly, through the series, as the material is tied to a progressive National Curriculum, and it does mean that reference can be made, both forward and backward, for more or less challenging activities for children to undertake.

ENGLISH

In order to match with children's increasing practical grasp of the mechanics of the English language, the range of literary experiences to which they should be exposed expands considerably in Year 3. Fiction, non-fiction, poetry, plays, ICT and specialised reference books all become part of the programme of work proposed by the National Literacy Strategy so that, even within the Literacy Hour, the value of experiential education is recognised. However, particularly at word level, there is a great deal of the nuts and bolts of language still to be taught.

In compiling these activities, we have followed our guiding principle of concentrating on what lends itself most readily to the worksheet format. Fortunately, this leaves a great deal of language work that can be tackled effectively. You will find a distinct bias towards word- and sentence-level work and less emphasis on text-level work where comprehension and composition really demand stimulus and experience not readily compressed into a single sheet of A4. Perhaps more importantly, text-level work can also benefit greatly from adult intervention and social interaction.

As reading skills develop, there are increasing opportunities for children to work on their own, and many of the following sheets can be used for independent work. You may well find that more practice is needed of a particular area of learning; hopefully, some of the sheets will give you ideas and formats that you can use to produce extra material in a similar form, where needed. Where appropriate, we have provided some useful pointers in these notes.

For further details of the teaching programme, apart from *The National Curriculum* and the *National Literacy Strategy* itself, you should consult other relevant government publications, in particular those published by the Standards and Effectiveness Unit. Although the range of some of the publications can be off-putting where it encompasses more than one key stage, they do contain useful material. See, for example, *The NLS Word Level Work Activity Resource Bank, Module 2*, published jointly by DfES and OUP.

Words in words (1) (page 14)

Objective: To look for examples of short words within long words.

What to do: Before working on the sheet, do a similar exercise with the whole class on the board: *How many words can you find in 'gone'?* (*go, on, one*.) Make sure the children understand the principle that they do not mix the letters up to make anagrams. When completing the sheet, they should find that they are provided with the correct number of spaces to match the number of words possible. (*Nothing: no, not, thing, thin, in; themselves: them, the, he, elves, hem; clothes: clot, lot, the, cloth, he; everlasting: ever, last, tin, eve, sting, as, in; together: to, get, the, he, her; tog* and *ether* are also possible.)

Differentiation: Children who need support may work better in pairs for this activity.

Extension: Play a game of 'Hunt the word'. Ask the children to hunt for the dictionary word that has the greatest number of words within it. If you run this as a competition, make sure that all of the children use the same type of dictionary.

Words in words (2) (page 15)

Objective: To look for examples of short words within long words.

What to do: See the notes for 'Words in words (1)', above.

Differentiation/extension: These will be the same as 'Words in words (1)'.

Compounds in the playground (page 16)

Objective: To recognise compound words.

What to do: Make sure that the children have been taught how to recognise a compound word. Show them some obvious examples, such as *blackboard, classroom* and *playground*. Ask the children to search the picture on the sheet for compounds and then write them in the spaces provided. The children may find more compound-word objects than there are writing spaces – reward their perceptiveness! They should find: *playground,* *hopscotch, football, gatepost, handstand, raincoat, shoelace, netball, goalpost, lunchbox.*

Differentiation: Again, this is an activity where some children will benefit from working in a supportive group. Working in pairs is probably best.

Extension: Ask the children to think of groups of compound words containing a common word, for example *over* (*overcome, overcast, overcoat, overdue, overladen, overtime, overhead*) or *news* (*newscaster, newsreader, newspaper* and so on).

Compounds in the kitchen (page 17)

Objective: To recognise compound words.

What to do: This follows a similar format to 'Compounds in the playground', so follow those notes, although the children are not prompted by writing spaces next to the objects they are looking for. The words are: *teaspoon, teapot, tablecloth, teacup, lampshade, saucepan, cupboard, corkscrew, noticeboard.*

Differentiation/extension: These can be the same as 'Compounds in the playground', above.

New words for old (page 18)

Objective: To recognise and construct compound words.

What to do: This follows on from earlier work on compound words. This time, children invent compound words that accurately convey meaning. Follow up the work by sharing some of the answers with the class. Can the children guess what object is being described from the invented compound word alone? Discuss meanings – most compound words are constructed to convey a word picture of the object so named, such as *sandcastle.*

Differentiation: Small groups will generate more possible answers and less able children will benefit from working in this way. More able children could try writing sentences containing as many compound words as possible: *The bookworm lay sideways in an overcoat on the sunbed at the airport under an overcast sky.*

Extension: Challenge the children to invent several alternatives for each answer. They might also be able to write dictionary definitions to match the new compound word.

The silence in lambs (page 19)

Objective: To examine, read and spell words containing silent letters.

What to do: First, the children must be aware that there are words in which certain letters remain silent, such as *wrist* and *knock*. Look for the silent letter in *lamb* as a group or class exercise, then let the children

examine the words on the sheet. This should be fairly straightforward, and the real challenge is to find other words to list at the bottom of the sheet. Encourage the children to use dictionaries for this.

Differentiation: Less able children may need adult intervention to sound out the words correctly and assist them in learning to discriminate and analyse the sounds they hear. Paired working is advisable for some children.

Extension: Ask the children to keep a scribble pad or notebook in which they write down words with silent letters that they come across in their reading. You might want to make a class chart of these, sorting the words into groups, such as *kn* words, *wr* words, *mb* words and so on.

Word blender (page 20)

Objective: To combine phonemes for reading and segment words to aid spelling.

What to do: Tell the children to mix and match the phonemes on the sheet to generate words (and non-words, such as *bround*, to reinforce awareness of legitimate spelling patterns). How many real words can they make?

Differentiation: Some children may need the support offered by working in a group. The activity can be made more interesting if the blending becomes a physical exercise. Mount the parts of words on strips of card and make interlocking tubes that can be rotated to generate words.

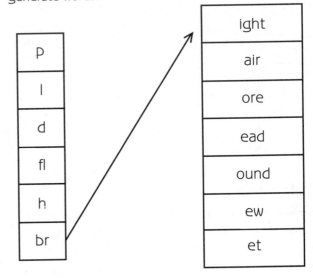

Similarly, you could make word slides, window strips and word wheels.

Extension: This is only one example of segmenting and blending words. The National Literacy Strategy suggests revision and consolidation of work done in Year 2 to identify and blend phonemes and segment words, so you could create further work of a similar sort, by referring to the lists of phonemes given in Appendix List 3 of the Strategy.

Put back the missing 'le' (page 21)

Objective: To investigate and learn words with the spelling pattern *le*.

What to do: Demonstrate the severing of *le* from a word. (For example, tell the children they are going to do a *simp* worksheet.) You could use scissors to literally sever the *le* from *muddle* as in the example on the sheet. Tell the children to read each sentence out loud and to work out where the *le* has been missed out. There is sufficient space in the text for them to add the missing letters.

Differentiation: You might allow some children to collect *le* words first, by searching their reading books, in order to prepare them for the exercise. Working in a supportive group is valuable.

Extension: Provide another missing ending for children to search for, such as the digraphs *ow*, *ir* and *er*.

'Re' chart (page 22)

Objective: To recognise and spell the common prefix *re* and to understand how its use influences meaning.

What to do: For this activity, the children need to simply fix the prefix and generate the new word. This should follow an explanation of what a prefix is. (Children should learn and use the term.) Let the children find their own word to include at the bottom of the sheet. The key to understanding here will be in the follow-up discussion, so talk about the new words. *How has the meaning changed from the old word?*

Differentiation: Most of the children should be capable of doing the simple first phase of this activity unaided. Allow the use of dictionaries, especially when the children are searching for a word to put in the empty box.

Extension: Children could write definitions for the words generated. They could rewrite a paragraph from a book putting *re* in front of each of the verbs. What strange words and amusing meanings result?

'Un' web (page 23)

Objective: To recognise and spell the common prefix *un* and to understand how its use influences meaning.

What to do: Ask the children to follow the web strands to create new words with prefixes attached. As in the previous sheet, the children should add a word of their own in the blank section of the web. Follow this up with discussion and analysis as with the previous activity.

Differentiation: Allow the use of dictionaries where necessary, although most children should be able to manage this activity without support.

Extension: Give children a piece of writing with the adjectives underlined. Let them add the *un* prefix and see what amusing nonsense results. You could encourage more able children to identify the adjectives for themselves.

Where's 'y'? (page 24)

Objective: To recognise and use a common suffix and understand how its use influences meaning and spelling.

What to do: Look at some examples of words with the suffix *y*, paying particular attention to how the spelling of the root word can be changed when adding this suffix, for example *bone – bony*, *mud – muddy*. In the activity on this sheet, the children are required to rewrite the sentences, changing the word by adding the suffix.

Differentiation: Let the children refer to dictionaries, but encourage more able children to try the exercise without using a dictionary.

Extension: Pin up a picture, for example of a racing car, or place an object in front of the children. Ask them to describe it using a word with the *y* suffix (*speedy*, *shiny*, *noisy* and so on). You could provide a different object for each group and then pass them on to see how many different words the whole class can come up with.

Weather forecast (page 25)

Objectives: To recognise and spell words containing a common suffix; to identify root words; to understand how the use of the suffix influences meaning.

What to do: This activity can be seen as a reverse of 'Where's 'y'?', above. This time, the children are asked to identify the root word.

Differentiation: Provide dictionaries for less able children to check their answers for correct spelling.

Extension: Help children to keep a weather record for a week or so (repetition at different times of the year is a good idea). See how many *y* adjectives can be used in the descriptions.

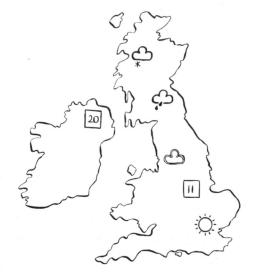

Suffix chains (page 26)

Objectives: To recognise and spell words containing common suffixes; to identify root words; to understand how the use of the suffix influences meaning.

What to do: Examine an example of a suffix chain with the class, such as *merciless – mercy – merciful*. Help the children to realise how the meaning of the root word *mercy* is changed by the addition of the suffixes. Explain to them that they are going to complete chains of their own on the sheet, by supplying the root word. There is also a blank for the children to choose their own root word and two chain words.

Differentiation: Encourage less able children to underline the root word in the examples completing the links. You might also want them to work in pairs.

Extension: Ask children to think of brief definitions of the three words in each chain. This could be done as an oral exercise or as homework.

Fixing suffixes (page 27)

Objective: To understand how words are changed when the suffixes *er* and *est* are added.

What to do: Examine the first example on the sheet that has been completed for the children and draw their attention to the relative sizes of the illustrations. Ask the children to complete the blanks with the appropriate comparative and superlative, using the suffixes *er* and *est*, then construct an example of their own. What happens to the spelling of the word when a suffix is added? Look at examples such as *happier* and *happiest*, *sadder* and so on. Can the children discover any rules for adding suffixes?

Differentiation: Some children will benefit from working co-operatively on this activity. Make sure they understand that the pictures provide useful clues.

Extension: Using dictionaries and fiction and non-fiction books to look through, ask children to prepare three lists containing other comparatives and superlatives generated by the use of the same suffixes, for example *big – bigger – biggest*, *clean – cleaner – cleanest* and so on. You could set this as a homework exercise, although you may wish to limit the number of words that the children should collect!

Step on the verb (page 28)

Objectives: To use the term *verb*; to identify verbs correctly.

What to do: Go through the photocopiable sheet with the children (you could make an OHT of it for this). Explain that the pirate must reach the treasure and not fall into the river where the crocodile waits to eat him. He can do this if the children colour the stepping-stones he should use, remembering that he can only tread on verbs. Ask the children to include the verbs in completing the sentence at the bottom of the sheet.

Differentiation: Less able readers should work in pairs or in small groups on this activity.

Extension: Verbs are 'doing' words, so let children 'do' by imitating the pirate in his search for the treasure. They must smile, cheer, search and so on. You could duplicate the sheet, but blank out the verbs and ask children to provide a new set of stepping-stones (verbs) that the pirate has to traverse to reach the treasure (for example, *faint, fly, gargle*). This is a possible homework task, and again, the children could have fun acting out the sequence.

Verbs on a feather (page 29)

Objectives: To use the term *verb*; to identify verbs correctly.

What to do: Having coloured in the verbs red, allow children to complete the head-dress using colours other than red.

Differentiation: Where children need help with reading, allow them to work co-operatively. If they struggle to identify verbs, ask them to check each word to see if it is possible to 'do' it. *Can you 'sing'? Yes, so a verb. Can you 'behind'? No, so not a verb.* (In common parlance you can 'down' a drink, but the children are unlikely to pick up on this one! If they do, give them credit for it if they can explain their answer.)

Extension: Provide a blank copy of the head-dress and ask the children to supply each feather with a verb, limiting the choice of verbs to those used to report speech only (such as *said, exclaimed* and *answered*) or those used in sport (*threw, swam, hurled* and so on) or some similar limiting constraint. This could be another homework task.

Where's the verb? (page 30)

Objective: To learn about the function of verbs in a sentence and notice that sentences cannot make sense without them.

What to do: Illustrate the activity by going through an example with the class, such as *I ___ my dinner at lunchtime.* The children need to understand that to make sense, a sentence needs to include a verb. Ask the children to read the 'sentences' on the sheet, then rewrite them, adding the missing verb. All the examples are taken from nursery rhymes or games and should not pose much difficulty nor encourage too wide a range of alternative verbs (such as *Mary ate a little lamb*).

Differentiation: For those children who have difficulty reading the phrases, working in pairs may be the best solution.

Extension: Children could write out a passage from a book, missing out all the verbs, and then read it to the class. Can other children provide the missing verb? Alternatively, provide a passage without verbs and ask children to include a suitable verb to make the passage make sense.

Missing verbs (page 31)

Objective: To use verb tenses with increasing accuracy – to use the past tense consistently.

What to do: Explain to the children that they should choose verbs from the list that match the actions in the pictures, and that the verbs should all be in the past tense. Point out that the verbs don't all have *ed* spellings and that the present tense versions of the verbs are there too.

Differentiation: Make this a group activity for those children that require more help.

Extension: Repeat the activity, but this time ask the children to provide their own past tense verbs to complete the sentences. Let them have fun with this, provided the sentence is completed with a verb of the right tense and makes some sort of sense. For example, *When the cat jumped, the dog giggled* would be acceptable, whereas *When the cat jumped, the dog faint* would not be.

'ing' wheel (page 32)

Objective: To learn the conventions of spelling – how the spelling of a verb alters when *ing* is added.

What to do: This activity is quite straightforward, although it would be worth going over an example with the children first, such as *work – working, hope – hoping, beg – begging*, to help them understand that they are looking for a spelling change in the root part of the word.

Differentiation: Word banks or dictionaries should be provided for less able children.

Extension: Challenge the children to make an *ing* wheel of their own, using different verbs.

Computer error (page 33)

Objectives: To use verb tenses consistently in writing; to extend the vocabulary of verbs used to introduce and conclude dialogue.

What to do: Read the story on the sheet to the class. You could do this with appropriate dramatic emphasis, but still use the word *said*. Ask the children if they think anything is wrong with the way the story is written. Can they improve anything about it? Would the drowning girl really *say* 'Help!'? The children can write their choice of verbs over the words on the sheet, but you may prefer them to rewrite the whole text. Alternatively, this could be a word-processing task in which the children alter the text on screen.

Differentiation: Supervised group work is the preferred differentiation for less able children.

Extension: An on-screen version of the sheet would enable children to experiment with swapping the verbs around and trying out others.

Synonym search (page 34)

Objectives: To understand the term *synonym*; to generate synonyms for high-frequency words.

What to do: To help the children understand what synonyms are, use fairly obvious examples of both nouns and verbs (*go, leave, depart* and so on). *Nice* is a tricky word because, along with its 'fine' meaning, it can take on a number of meanings depending upon context. However, it is a word used and overused by children (and adults) and this exercise is aimed at opening their eyes to some alternatives. Make sure that the children understand how a wordsearch works and point out that some words are written backwards and diagonal. Advise them to ring the words as they find them. As a class exercise, get the children to suggest some alternative words for *nice* before they start. The hidden words are: *enjoyable, pretty, polite, lovely, fine, superb, delightful, good, splendid.*

Differentiation: If this activity is undertaken by children who have been introduced to a thesaurus, allow those that would benefit to have access to one. The puzzle will be made easier if small groups work on it co-operatively.

ENGLISH

Extension: This sheet is just a beginning. If you are happy that children understand what a synonym is, give them other high-frequency words from the list in the Literacy Strategy (such as *nasty* and *little*) to investigate, using a thesaurus if necessary. This could be a challenge for homework. Another possible homework task could be to ask children to put each word from the wordsearch into a sentence. You could play a game with the children where you occasionally stop what you are saying and ask for a synonym of a word you have just used. For example, *We are going to walk across the playground. What word could I use instead of 'walk'?* (Stroll, amble, stride, march and so on.) Don't be frightened of extending the children's vocabulary range with new words.

Lists of opposites (page 35)

Objective: To explore antonyms.

What to do: Children will need to have been taught what an antonym is before working on this activity, but it is a straightforward worksheet.

Differentiation: Some children will find this exercise difficult and group work with a supporting adult is the best solution. The group can test out solutions orally and have assistance in using the reference books.

Extension: Children could be given high-frequency words from the Literacy Strategy list to find antonyms for. Start an "andy antonym' chart on the wall.

DIY dictionary (1) (page 36)

Objective: To write definitions of words, developing accuracy and expression.

What to do: All of the children should have plenty of practice in using a dictionary. Play games with them. Say, for example, *I have just arrived from outer space and I don't know what an orange is. What does the dictionary tell me?* When you are confident that they understand what a definition is, introduce the sheet and explain what they have to do. Encourage brevity. Who can write the shortest good definition?

Differentiation: Use adult support to help the less able. Encourage them to give oral definitions before writing.

Extension: Provide the children with some definitions from their dictionaries and ask them to work out what word is being defined. This could be a good homework task.

DIY dictionary (2) (page 37)

Objective: To write definitions of words, developing accuracy and expression.

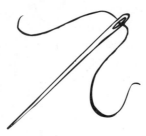

What to do: See the notes for 'DIY dictionary (1),' above. Children might be amused by this definition of *net: a series of holes joined together with string.* They might enjoy making up similar 'nonsense' definitions.

Differentiation/extension: These will be the same as 'DIY dictionary (1)', above.

The long and short of it (page 38)

Objective: To use the apostrophe to spell shortened forms of words.

What to do: Ensure that the children understand what contractions are and let them search for these in their reading books. Talk about their findings. Watch out for the possessive apostrophe and that the children don't confuse the two.

Differentiation: Most children should be able to complete the activity unaided, but some may find it helpful to work in groups.

Extension: Challenge children to find other examples of contracted words that involve the use of an apostrophe. It would be helpful to put up a class chart of the most common ones.

Making plurals (page 39)

Objective: To investigate the rules for generating plurals of common nouns.

What to do: Point out that the nouns have been grouped according to how their plurals are formed. The real challenge here is for the children to be able to extract the general rules from the specific examples as this will help them when they come across plurals of less common nouns.

Differentiation: Less able children should be able to suggest their answers orally before writing them down. Dictionaries may be used as aids. Encourage more able children to write down the rules rather than just be aware of them.

Extension: Challenge children to search a page or chapter of a book to identify plurals that follow the rules illustrated on this sheet. This could be a homework task.

Odd plurals (page 40)

Objectives: To recognise that some plurals do not comply with common rules; to use the terms *singular* and *plural* correctly.

What to do: Make sure the children understand that although there are rules for making plurals, there are some words that are not law abiding.

Differentiation: Help less able children to investigate answers using a dictionary. You may also want them to work in groups or with the attention of an adult.

Extension: A good homework task would be to initiate a search for plural law-breakers – challenge children to find other plurals that break the rules.

Ten to Tooting (page 41)

Objectives: To write poetry that uses sound to create effects; to use alliteration.

What to do: Tackle this activity as an oral class exercise first. Demonstrate the alliterative sounds (though you may not want to use the term *alliteration* at this stage). Who can come up with the most successful and outrageous suggestions for the next lines? Then let the children work on the sheet on their own, adding illustrations as they go. Encourage them to sound out their lines to make sure that they have continued the alliterative effect.

Differentiation: For less able children, this can be approached as a group or pair activity. You could enlarge the sheet to allow two to work on it at the same time.

Extension: More able children will be capable of extending the lines of the poem with further information, still using alliteration, for example *One wiggly worm wearing a worn woolly, Two terrible toads tickling tiny termites* and so on.

Confusing cuttings (1) (page 42)

Objective: To distinguish between *fiction* and *non-fiction* and to use the terms correctly.

What to do: The sheet assumes that the children already understand the difference between fiction and non-fiction. Suggest to the children that once they have decided which is which, they re-read the extracts on the sheet to look for the characteristics that helped them come to their decisions.

Differentiation: Struggling readers will need support. An adult could read the passages to a group and discuss possible answers.

Extension: Children can be challenged to find examples of fiction and non-fiction in the classroom. You could start classified lists of the different types (for example, plays, stories, poems, recipes, car manuals, information books, dictionaries, myths, fables, instruction leaflets, newspapers). They could then write

a piece of non-fiction or fiction – the rules to a playground game, for example.

Confusing cuttings (2) (page 43)

Objective: To distinguish between *fiction* and *non-fiction* and to use the terms correctly.

What to do: See the notes for 'Confusing cuttings (1)', above.

Differentiation/extension: These will be the same as 'Confusing cuttings (1)'.

Off-the-peg rhymes (page 44)

Objective: To write a simple rhyming poem.

What to do: Make sure the children understand that the words for the missing rhymes are hanging on the washing line at the top of the sheet. Go through the first couple of lines of the poem as a class, emphasising the rhyme within the line. Can the children match the rhymes correctly? Then ask them to complete the sheet.

Differentiation: Provide help with identifying the objects on the line if required. If children struggle to hear the rhymes, place them in a group and give adult support to sound out the lines of the poem as they are completed to make sure that the rhyme works.

Extension: Encourage confident children to compose a poem on the same lines unaided. For example, *On Monday... Cuddly Ken ate a hen* and so on.

Crash chaos (page 45)

Objective: To recount events in the style of a newspaper report.

What to do: Show the class some examples of headlines and reports from newspapers. Draw their attention to the headline on the sheet and tell them that they should write a brief report on the accident. The only evidence they have to go on is the photograph. Explain that they should examine the picture for details and evidence to use in their report.

Differentiation: Provide different writing options. Some children could use a word processor, some could benefit from using an enlarged sheet to write on. Poor writers could dictate their report into a tape recorder (like a reporter) and then be given help with making a written record.

Extension: Challenge the children to write about the accident in a different way, such as in a letter to a friend, as a story or a play.

Words in words (1)

How many words can you find in...

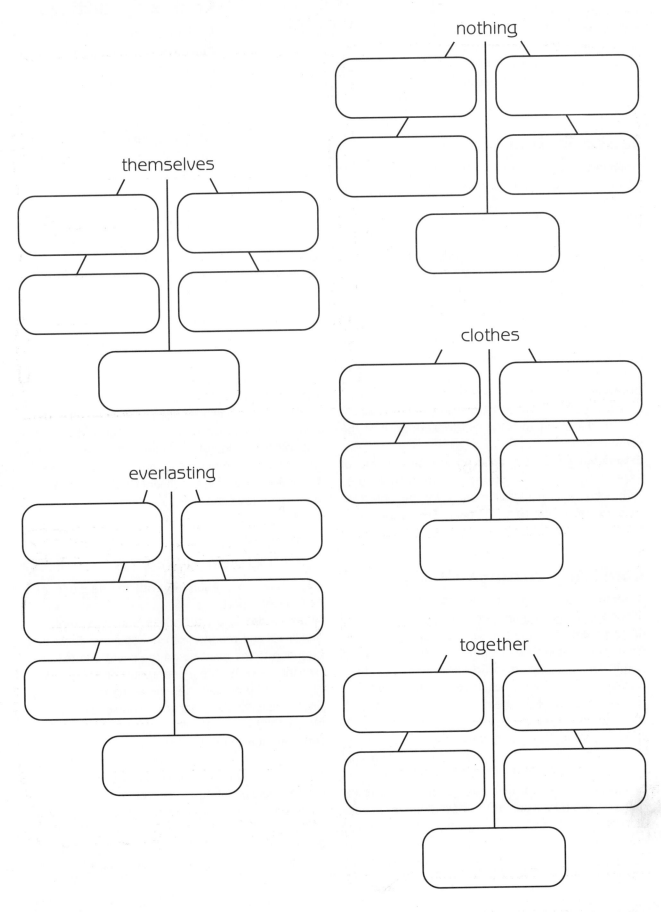

Words in words (2)

How many words can you find in…

cupboard

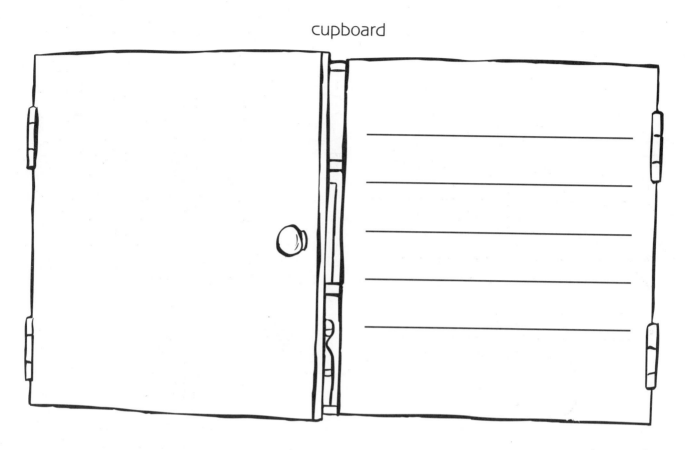

wardrobe

underwear

PHOTOCOPIABLE

Compounds in the playground

Find as many compound words as you can in this picture.

SCHOLASTIC

Compounds in the kitchen

How many compound words can you spot in this kitchen?

Compound word list

_____   _____

_____   _____

_____   _____

_____   _____

_____

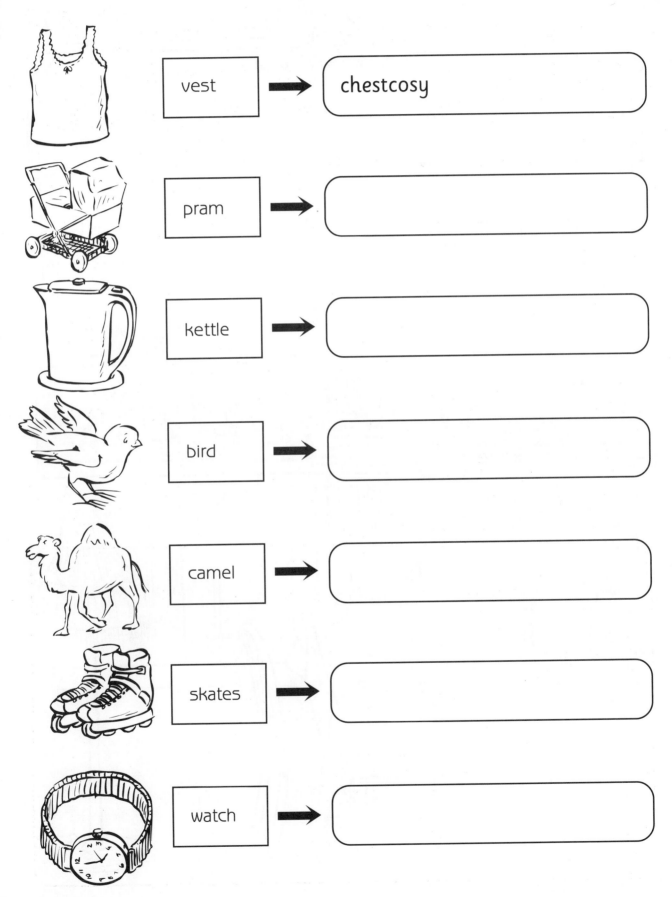

New words for old

Make new compound words to replace these words. The first one has been done for you.

vest → chestcosy

pram →

kettle →

bird →

camel →

skates →

watch →

The silence in lambs

Lam(b) has a silent letter **(b)**.

● Say these words, then circle the silent letters.

write   lamb   gnat

wrong   knife   know

                                               wring

         sign   wriggle

gnaw   hymn

              bomb

     knee   rhyme

● Can you find more words with silent letters?

Word blender

Make words and non-words, and list them in the table. One has been done as an example.

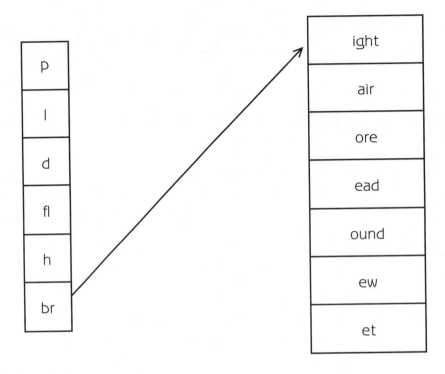

Words	Non-words
bright	

Put back the missing 'le'

Someone has made a **mudd le** by cutting **le** off the ends of words.

Put them back in where they belong.

Doctor Foster fell in a pudd   up to his midd   .

Didd   didd   dumpling, my son John…

The cat and the fidd   , the cow jumped over the moon.

When the wind blows, the crad   will rock.

Litt   Miss Muffet sat on a tuffet.

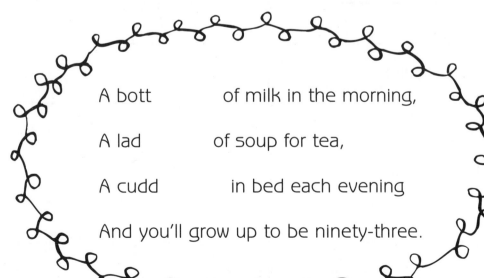

A bott   of milk in the morning,

A lad   of soup for tea,

A cudd   in bed each evening

And you'll grow up to be ninety-three.

'Re' chart

Complete this chart using the prefix **re** to make new words. Add one of your own at the bottom. Think about what the new words mean.

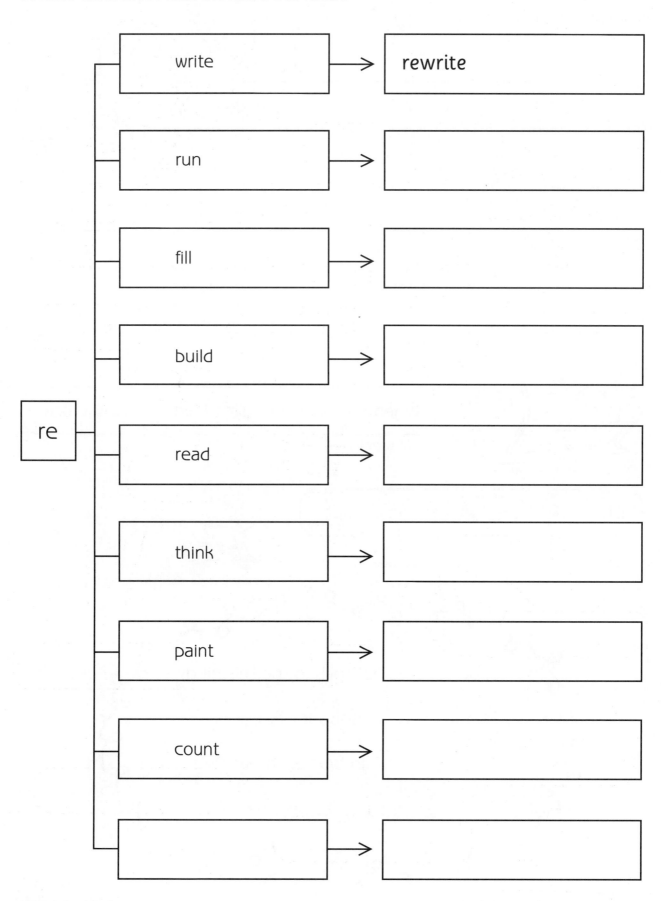

re		
write	→	rewrite
run	→	
fill	→	
build	→	
read	→	
think	→	
paint	→	
count	→	
	→	

'Un' web

● Complete this web using the prefix **un**. Think about what the new words mean.
● Add one of your own.

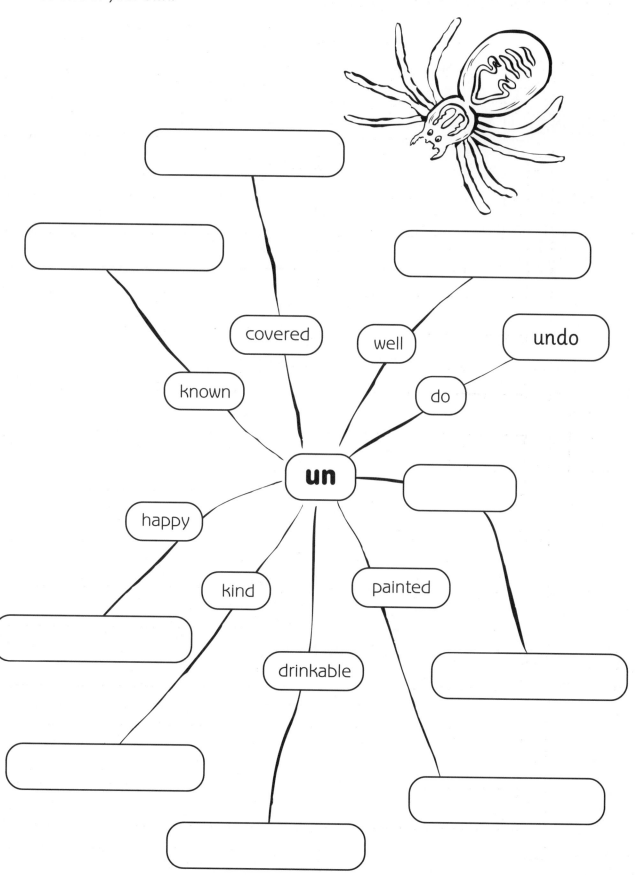

covered

well

undo

known

do

un

happy

kind

painted

drinkable

Where's 'y'?

Use the suffix **y** to make sense of these sentences. Write them out correctly. Watch out – the root word sometimes changes.

It was a **cloud** day.

_____

The clown was very **fun**.

_____

My fish seemed very **smell**.

_____

We picnicked on the **grass** bank.

_____

Our cat has a **bone** back.

_____

The **noise** jet zoomed overhead.

_____

Weather forecast

The suffix **y** is used often in this weather forecast. Write out the root words.

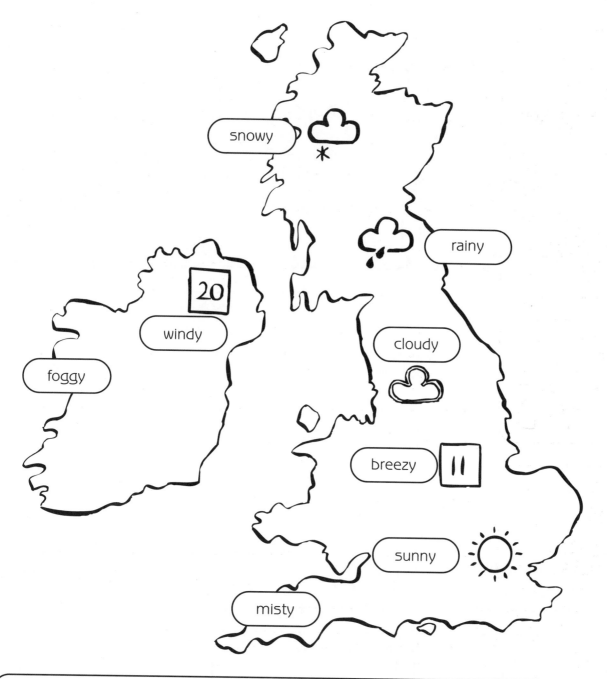

snowy

rainy

windy

cloudy

foggy

breezy

sunny

misty

Root words

m_____ f_____ su_____ sn_____

w_____ c_____ r_____ b_____

■SCHOLASTIC   **25**

Suffix chains

● These words use the suffixes **ful** and **less**. Write the missing root-word link.

hopeless	hope	hopeful
helpless		helpful
thankless		thankful
useless		useful
thoughtless		thoughtful
careless		careful

● Write a chain of your own.

Fixing suffixes

● Fix the suffixes **er** and **est** to these words. The first one has been done for you.

wide	wider	widest
close		
small		
happy		
sad		

● Add **er** and **est** to a word of your own.

Step on the verb

Colour over the verbs to help the pirate reach the treasure.

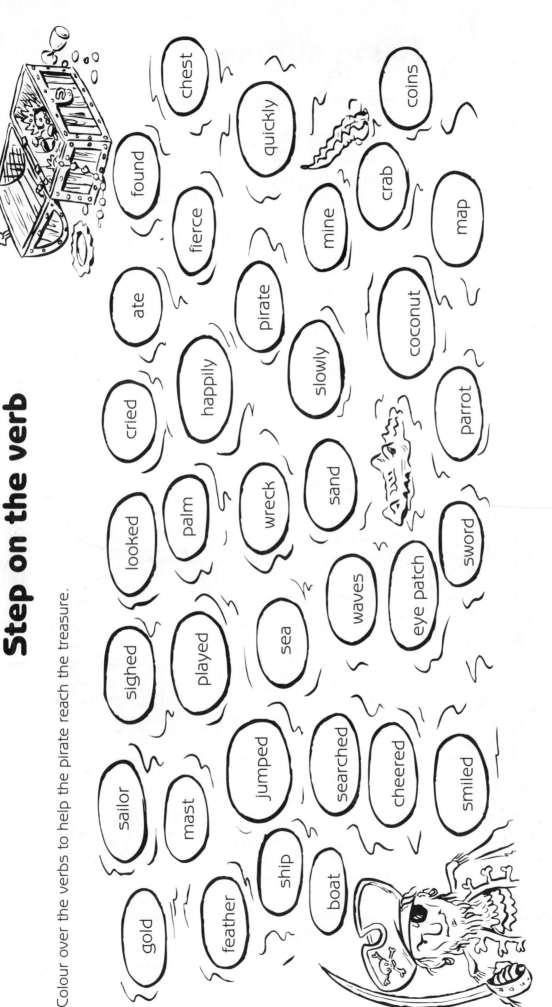

The pirate **smiled,** _____

_____ and **found** the treasure.

Colour the verb feathers red.

Verbs on a feather

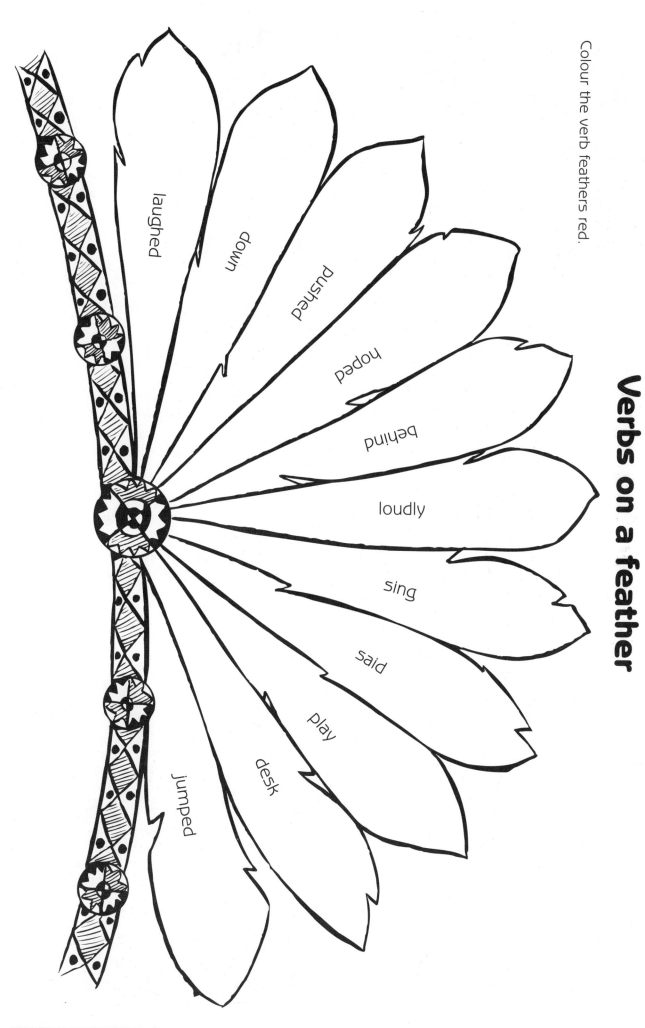

laughed

down

pushed

hoped

behind

loudly

sing

said

play

desk

jumped

Where's the verb?

Put in the missing verb so that these sentences make sense.

Jack and Jill up the hill.

_____

Mary a little lamb.

_____

Little Jack Horner in a corner.

_____

Who Cock Robin?

_____

Humpty Dumpty on a wall.

_____

I with my little eye…

_____

Hickory dickory dock
The mouse up the clock.

_____

_____

Missing verbs

Martin _____ into the sea.

The teacher _____ when she saw the mouse.

The boy _____ like a pig.

When the cat jumped, the dog _____

The children _____ at the camera.

Daisy _____ her bike all the way home.

Choose the correct verbs to fill the spaces.

(eat)   (ate)   (ride)   (smile)   (rode)   (bark)

(dive)   (screamed)   (dived)   (barked)   (smiled)   (scream)

'ing' wheel

When you add **ing** to a verb, the spelling of the verb sometimes changes. Add **ing** to these words and put the new words in the correct list.

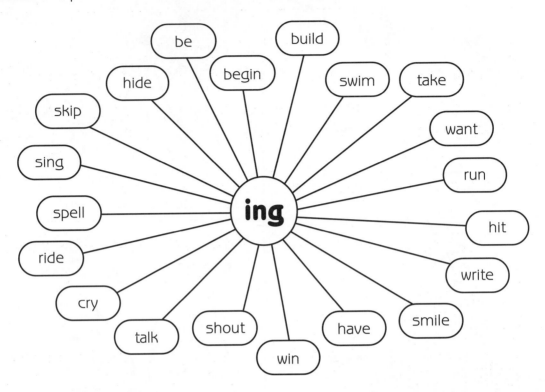

Change	No change
riding	spelling

Computer error

This computer can only use **said** when reporting speech. Replace **said** with better verbs.

"Help!" **said** the girl as she fell into the sea.

A man **said**, "Call the coastguard!"

"Where is the lifebelt?" **said** the woman on the pier.

"Help! Help!" the girl **said** again as the waves

crashed over her head.

Her friend was crying. "I told her not to do a

handstand on the rocks," she **said**.

"Keep calm!" **said** the policeman. "I'm

coming." He dived into the sea. "Hold on to my

waist," he **said** above the noise of the waves.

At that moment the fin of a shark appeared. "Oh no," **said** her

friend. The watching crowd **said**, "Hurry!"

Helpful verbs

(shouted) (cried) (asked) (exclaimed) (called) (commanded)

(enquired) (instructed) (muttered) (repeated) (screamed)

M SCHOLASTIC

Synonym search

Synonyms are words that share the same or similar meanings, for example:

small and **little**,

shout and **yell**.

How many synonyms for **nice** can you find in this puzzle?

a	e	n	j	o	y	a	b	l	e
x	y	t	t	e	r	p	p	d	l
l	o	v	e	l	y	o	e	o	v
b	c	u	r	n	w	l	n	x	o
r	y	b	r	c	s	i	i	s	m
d	e	l	i	g	h	t	f	u	l
w	n	t	f	v	o	e	m	p	n
s	c	i	l	l	i	o	q	e	t
s	r	z	c	b	c	y	d	r	a
d	i	d	n	e	l	p	s	b	s

Lists of opposites

Antonyms are words with opposite meanings, for example **hot** and **cold**, **up** and **down**.
Use a thesaurus and a dictionary to find as many antonyms as you can for these words.

happy
unhappy sad miserable

polite

DIY dictionary (1)

Write and illustrate your own dictionary.

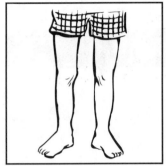

leg in humans, one of two lower limbs, used
for moving and holding up the body

lemon _____

_____

_____

_____

letter _____

_____

_____

_____

life-jacket _____

_____

_____

_____

lion _____

_____

_____

_____

DIY dictionary (2)

Write and illustrate your own dictionary.

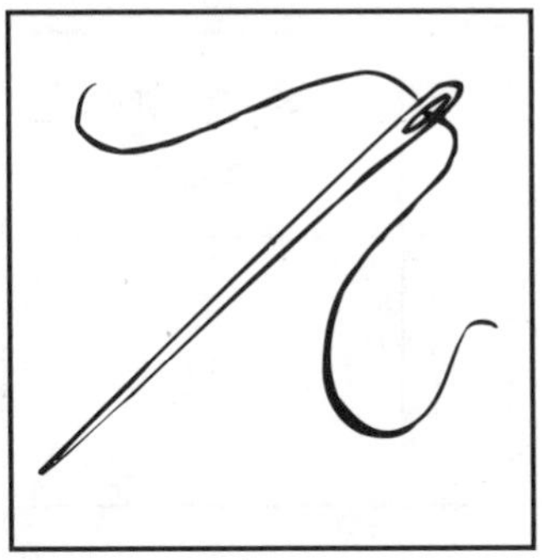

needle <u>a sharp, pointed, thin piece of</u>

<u>metal with an eye in it for thread to pass</u>

<u>through; used for sewing</u>

neigh _____

neighbour _____

nest _____

net _____

The long and short of it

An **apostrophe** can be used to replace a letter or letters and so shorten a word. Complete the chart.

▬ becomes ➡		apostrophe (') replaces
do not	➡ don't	o
will not	➡	
would not	➡	
cannot	➡	
are not	➡	
it is	➡	
there is	➡	
who is	➡	
he is	➡	
she is	➡	

Making plurals

● Complete these lists of plurals.

One apple, many _apples_

One bag, many _____

One cup, many _____

One dog, many _____

One egg, many _____

One frog, many _____

One goat, many _____

● How did you make these plurals?

A box – some _boxes_

A church – some _____

A dish – some _____

A fox – some _____

A glass – some _____

A dress – some _____

A wish – some _____

● How did you make these plurals?

● How do these plurals work?

story  _____   baby  _____

fairy ➡ _____   lady ➡ _____

body _____   party  _____

Odd plurals

What are the plurals?

a sheep

some _____

one half

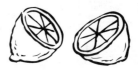

two _____

a man

several _____

a child

many _____

one tooth

lots of _____

one fish

many _____

a mouse

some _____

Ten to Tooting

● Read and finish this poem. Listen for the sounds at the start of the words.

● Illustrate your poem in the frame.

One wiggly worm,

Two terrible toads,

Three _____,

Four _____,

Five _____,

Six _____,

Seven _____,

Eight _____,

Nine _____,

Ten _____,

turned up in Tooting.

Tooting

ENGLISH PHOTOCOPIABLE

Confusing cuttings (1)

Read these cuttings. Which are fiction and which non-fiction? Explain how you can tell.

The woodcutter took his axe and chopped down the door. Then he started on Grandma. Luckily, Grandma was really the wolf in her nightie. So Little Red Riding Hood was safe and the wolf was dead.

_____

_____

Wolves hunt together in packs. They are dog-like animals with grey fur and upright ears. They are carnivorous.

_____

_____

On Wednesday, Manchester United had a lucky escape. They were saved from defeat by Nantes when they scored a penalty in extra time.

_____

_____

The sky glowed red. A green creature appeared from behind a rock. In the red light it was beautiful and horrible at the same time. Its legs and arms were tied in a confused knot. Then it spoke: "Take me to your leader."

_____

_____

Confusing cuttings (2)

Can you tell non-fiction from fiction? Explain how.

 Put the fish in the pan. Pour 1 pint of stock over it and boil for 20 minutes.

_____

_____

 Most teachers know how to teach spelling, but need to spend more time on teaching sentence-level skills.

_____

_____

In the corner was a seat. Jack sat on it with a Christmas pie on his lap. He had forgotten his spoon, so had to use his thumb instead. He stuck a plumb on his thumb and said, "What a good boy am I?"

_____

_____

 Most modern cars use unleaded petrol. This helps to keep the air cleaner, which is a good thing for us and the environment in general.

_____

_____

Off-the-peg rhymes

Use the items on the washing line to complete the rhyming poem.

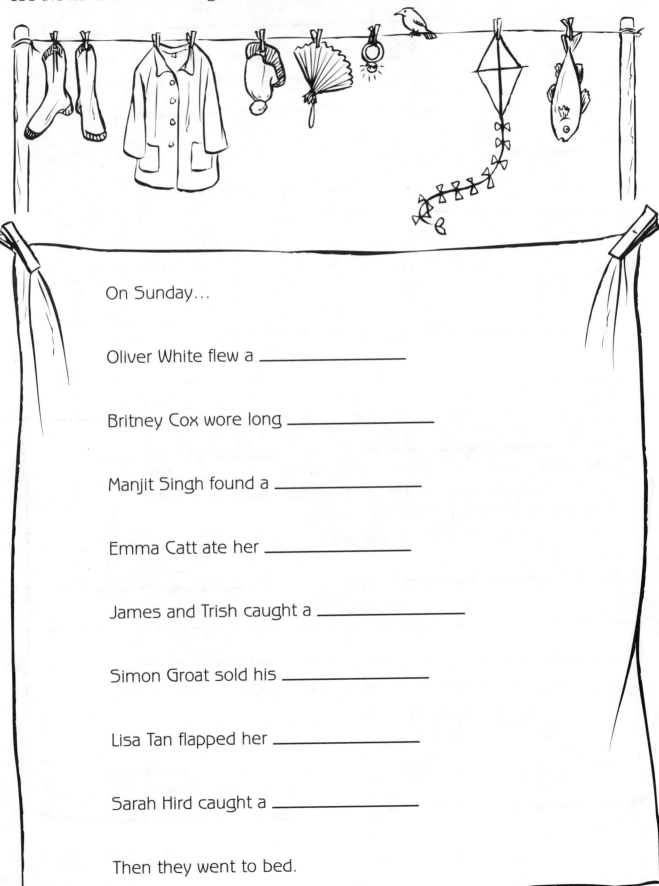

On Sunday…

Oliver White flew a _____

Britney Cox wore long _____

Manjit Singh found a _____

Emma Catt ate her _____

James and Trish caught a _____

Simon Groat sold his _____

Lisa Tan flapped her _____

Sarah Hird caught a _____

Then they went to bed.

Crash chaos

Look carefully at the photograph and write a newspaper report to go with it.

SCHOLASTIC **45**

MATHS

Pencil and paper procedures put in their first formal appearance in the Numeracy Strategy programme for Year 3 children, but this is not, of course, the first year in which children *record* mathematics. It may be the formal introduction of such procedures, but the methods suggested in the strategy are still only beginnings, not compact final-form written calculations. In the documentation they are even referred to as 'jottings' so the emphasis clearly remains on mental work. Written calculations should, in the words of the strategy, be used to 'support, record and explain' partial mental methods. With the photocopiable sheets in this section, we have not attempted to 'teach' mental calculation strategies and because choices had to be made – the curriculum contains so much – we have chosen to concentrate on those areas where the worksheet approach, rather than 'hands-on', is the most appropriate.

The best way to get a succinct overview of the mathematics programme for Year 3 children is to study the 13 bullet points compressed into half a page in Chapter 2 of the Numeracy Strategy. These identify the key objectives for the year. You can get further information from the following (and subsequent) publications: the *National Curriculum* and *The National Numeracy Strategy; Mathematical Vocabulary; Teaching Mental Calculation Strategies; Standards in Mathematics*.

Keeping count (page 53)

Objective: To extend number sequences, counting on or back in steps of 1, 10 or 100 from any two- or three-digit number.

What to do: The words *on* and *back* need to be thoroughly understood and it may be best to check by revising this sort of counting on a class number line before setting the children to work on the sheet. Discuss the patterns that emerge as the children colour the number square.

Differentiation: Some children may need a prop to tackle the first part of the sheet (although this is revision of earlier work) and you might want to provide an extended number line around the classroom or along a corridor. For very large numbers, children need to have grasped how the number system works and be able to extrapolate high numbers from low (67, 68, 69 hence 167, 168, 169 and so on). This may need specific teaching.

Extension: Ask children to respond orally to questions or commands such as: *Count on in tens from 40* or *Count back from 357 in tens.*

Big steps (page 54)

Objective: To extend number sequences, counting on or back in steps of 10 or 100 from any number.

What to do: Demonstrate to the children that this activity involves counting in tens and hundreds, both on and back. They should continue the sequences in the stepping stones and stepladder.

Differentiation: Less able children might need to work under adult supervision. They could count in ones for the first example, but should be taught to look for clues to a quicker way. Counting in ones for steps of 100 will take for ever!

Extension: Children need to be able to deal with questions like this speedily and orally, so provide plenty of quick practice.

Getting even (page 55)

Objective: To recognise odd and even numbers.

What to do: Colouring in the even numbers in the square on the sheet should pose no difficulty as this is revision of work covered previously, but ask the children to look closely at the sequences in order to make general statements about odd and even numbers.

Differentiation: After completing the first part of the activity, some children may benefit from adult intervention to notice the patterns they have made. Interrogate the sequences with the children and find as many ways as possible to confirm understanding of the patterns in their minds. Choose numbers at random and ask children to identify whether it is odd or even. Look at the sequence of endings.

Extension: Oral work involving a thorough understanding of odd and even is valuable. You could ask questions such as: *What is the next odd number after 117? How many even numbers lie between 31 and 39?*

The missing thinks (page 56)

Objectives: To describe and extend number sequences; to count on or back in steps of any size.

What to do: Practise sequences similar to those on the sheet as mental exercises first: *1, 3, 5, 7…* and so on. Make sure that children understand that they have to explain the rule for generating a number in the sequence. Accept correct explanations, however they are worded.

Differentiation: Allow less able children to refer to a number line if they struggle to complete the sequences.

Extension: Practise the same activity as a mental exercise only. Introduce the term *multiple*, asking, for example: *What do multiples of 5 end in?* Always look for children to explain sequences and to extract general rules where they exist.

Multiples

(page 57)

Objective: To recognise familiar multiples.

What to do: Practise how to

recognise multiples and confirm that the term *multiple* is understood before asking the children to work on the sheet. Show them how the first line of the rhyme is made up of multiples if they don't spot it themselves.

Differentiation: Most children should manage this sheet without support, but marking the multiples on a number line or hundred square is one way to help those who are struggling.

Extension: Using the examples of the rhymes on the sheet, set children the task of devising a rhyme for another chosen multiple, for example 3, 6, 9 I feel fine; 4, 8, 12, 16 My auntie's name is Christine.

Boxed in

(page 58)

Objective: To know what each digit of a number represents and to partition a number into multiples of 100, 10 and 1 (HTU).

What to do: Go through the completed example on the sheet and check that the children understand how the

number is 'broken down'. Stress *hundreds*, *tens* and *units* as terms. The children should then be able to complete the rest of the sheet unaided.

Differentiation: Partitioning numbers like this can be assisted by using apparatus such as Dienes Multibase (base 10) or abacuses. Put less able children in small groups with adult support.

Extension: Give children three digits and ask them to make the largest and smallest possible numbers with them. Practice like this will help to confirm understanding. For example, 6, 7 and 3 would give 763 and 367.

More or less? (page 59)

Objectives: To understand and use the vocabulary of comparing numbers; to understand how to use £ and p notation.

What to do: This activity is all about understanding vocabulary, so make sure that the children have plenty of experience of hearing and using the monetary terms in the classroom. Use the terms to revise HTU learning and introduce decimal notation. Completion of the sheet should then be straightforward.

Differentiation: Use apparatus to demonstrate the quantities where necessary. Less able children might find it helpful to use plastic money to compare £6.99 with £5.35, for example.

Extension: Provide more examples for children to compare using different measures, perhaps kilograms, centimetres, miles, euros.

Piggy in the middle (page 60)

Objective: To compare numbers and give a number that is halfway between them.

What to do: Before asking the children to work on this sheet, give them some mental practice at similar, though easier, problems. For example: *What is halfway between 10 and 12? What is halfway between 6 and 7? What is halfway between 10 and 20?* The sheet is completed by adding the missing number to the 'piggy in the middle'.

Differentiation: Allow less able children to use a number line or square.

Extension: Devise some practical problems involving a 'piggy in the middle' and some research, perhaps for homework. For example, *What is the middle numbered house in your street? What television programme is on BBC1 halfway between 3.30 and 5.30? What age lies halfway between your age and the Queen's?*

One hundred more or less

(page 61)

Objective: To say a number that is 100 more or 100 less than a given number.

What to do: Explain what the activity involves – adding or 'taking away' 100 each time. Completion of the boxes should not pose too many problems if the children have begun to grasp the concept of place value.

Differentiation: Less able children could set up the quantities using an abacus. Adding 100 should then be relatively easy.

Extension: It is not difficult to provide more practice by making a small modification to the sheet. Simply reverse the *more* and *less* and a page of new problems is created.

More or less: problems

(page 62)

Objective: To choose and use appropriate number operations to solve problems that involve understanding the vocabulary of comparison.

What to do: Really, these are straightforward 'sums', but the children have to read and understand the problem in order to get to the point where arithmetic can take over. This may be an activity that most of the children would tackle more confidently if working in small groups.

Differentiation: Let less able children work in pairs. Apparatus might help, for example 'toy' money for the money problem.

Extension: Working in pairs, ask children to devise a similar problem (they will also need to work out the answer) for their friend to solve.

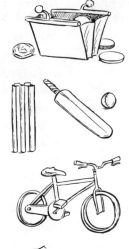

Keeping order (page 63)

Objective: To order a familiar set of numbers.

What to do: This is a straightforward ordering exercise and should not pose too many problems. If necessary, stress that it is the numbers that affect the answer, regardless of the units.

Differentiation: It may be necessary to assist some children with recording to avoid confusion. For example, suggest that they find the two extreme quantities first and cross out each quantity as it is placed in order so that they do not use any quantity twice.

Extension: This is a good opportunity to extend into work of a practical nature. For example, give children three objects to weigh and put in order of heaviness. Let them measure the lengths or widths of tables and desks and rank them in size order.

Points on a line (page 64)

Objective: To estimate the position of a point on a number line.

What to do: This activity is all about using the vocabulary of estimation, so discuss similar problems with the class and use words like *roughly, guess how many, nearest, close* and so on. *Estimate* is the key word so try to use it in preference to *guess*, which can imply wildness. (*Guess how old I am? 123?*) Answers that are roughly right are exactly right in this case! Hence answers around 7, 35, 54, and 90 are fine for the first section of the sheet.

Differentiation: Let those children who would benefit from it refer to a number line. They will still need to compare it with the line on the sheet and estimate the position of the arrow.

Extension: Cover all or part of the numbers on a number line. Challenge the children to estimate the position of an arrow and then let them compare their estimate with the actual number.

To the nearest 10

(page 65)

Objective: To round a number to the nearest 10.

What to do: Clearly, the children need to understand the concept and vocabulary of rounding before they tackle this activity, so practise a few examples together first. Make sure that the children understand the convention used here of rounding up quantities that are exactly halfway.

Differentiation: As long as the word *nearest* is understood, children should be able to complete this sheet as they can refer to the diagram and see that the arrow must be physically nearest to the ten at each end of the line. However, a little adult prompting may be required.

Extension: Provide similar examples without the support of the visual aid – the number line.

To the nearest 100 (page 66)

Objective: To round a number to the nearest 100.

What to do: This follows the same basic pattern as 'To the nearest 10', above, using larger quantities.

Differentiation/extension: These will be the same as 'To the nearest 10'.

Shady fractions (page 67)

Objective: To identify simple fractions and to recognise the equivalence between them.

What to do: Provided the children can read and understand the instructions, this sheet explains itself. There is no 'right' way to colour the squares and the children should explore this for themselves, working with simple fractions from experience, not calculations based on the recording system.

Differentiation: Let less confident children gain support by working in pairs or in a small group.

Extension: Providing as much practical experience of fractions as possible is the best extension to this sheet. Give children uniform-sized bricks or cubes and ask them to create a structure that is half one colour and half another. This could be varied to involve different fractions, for example one quarter red and three quarters blue.

Finding fractions (page 68)

Objective: To identify simple fractions.

What to do: This sheet should be self-explanatory, and is a simple matter of identification and experience.

Differentiation: Make this activity more 'hands-on' for less able children. The eggs, cups and bottles can be replicated using counting apparatus. Encourage children to physically divide up the sets of objects to ascertain the fractions involved in the examples.

Extension: Ask children to draw sets of objects and then illustrate some common fractions using their set: $\frac{1}{2}$, $\frac{1}{3}$, $\frac{1}{4}$, $\frac{2}{3}$, $\frac{1}{10}$ and so on. This could be an activity to be completed at home.

Working out fractions (page 69)

Objectives: To identify simple fractions and to recognise the equivalence between them; to estimate a fraction.

What to do: Make sure that the children understand that they only have to estimate the fractions shown in the last examples – not measure them accurately. Notice, however, that they *can* work out (without measuring) an exact fraction for the chocolates.

Differentiation: For the second part of the sheet, less able children might find it easier to work with a 30cm ruler marked in mm.

Extension: Get children to write down equivalent fractions of fractions they have become familiar with, for example that $\frac{5}{10}$ is the same as $\frac{1}{2}$. Ideally, provide them with apparatus that demonstrates this, such as equivalent fraction boards.

Sum totals (page 70)

Objective: To understand the operation of addition and that more than two numbers can be added together.

What to do: Make up some similar examples to do as a class before the children work on the sheet. Make sure the children understand they are working with whole numbers only, although give credit to children who suggest $51\frac{1}{2} + 48\frac{1}{2}$ or similar. The answers to the last problem are: 189, 216, 244, 128, 156, 209, 270, 217, 182, 163.

Differentiation: Unless children have progressed sufficiently in pencil and paper addition, the problem at the bottom of the page should be done as mental addition or using apparatus (counters or a number line). Support children in recording their working out as they go along, so they should add two numbers first (and record their answer) so that they are always dealing with the addition of two numbers. Thus (mentally) 104 + 16 + 69 might be *69 + 16 is 70 + 10 + 5 = 85 then add 104 = 189.*

Extension: Provide sentences like those on the sheet, with one 'blank' completed, for example *67 + □ = 100* and ask children to complete them as arithmetic, without a number line. This kind of practice can also be done as an oral exercise with the whole class. Ask, for example: *What do I need to add to 46 to make 100?*

Meaty sums (page 71)

Objectives: To understand the operation of addition and that more than two numbers can be added together; to test this understanding in a practical context.

What to do: Explain the idea of a shopping bill/receipt to the children. This activity may usefully be done using coins and toy money, if necessary. The answers depend upon the choice of items.

Differentiation: Children could play out this sheet in a class shop. Most children will benefit from using currency even if it is not real.

Extension: Provide shopping practice in a class shop, or you could take small groups of children on a shopping expedition with the object of buying provisions for a baking session, for example. Follow school guidelines on taking children out of school.

Double trouble (page 72)

Objective: To derive quickly addition doubles in multiples of 5 to 100.

What to do: You might do the first part of the sheet with all of the children and then look at how other doubles can be derived from them for the second part. (For example: *If you know that 20 + 20 = 40 and that 1 + 1 = 2 then 19 + 19 is 40 – 2 = 38.*) Similarly the children can use knowledge of doubles of multiples of 5 to complete the third section of the sheet. The children's example explanation (not for every sum – one will do!) should be given verbally to an adult.

Differentiation: Encourage children that need support to use paper to record their thinking, so, for example: 55 + 55 = 50 + 50 + 5 + 5 = 100 + 10 = 110.

Extension: Challenge children to learn doubles by heart. Select a few at a time, such as multiples of 5 from 5 + 5 to 50 + 50. You could set something like this for homework.

Hundreds that make a thousand (page 73)

Objective: To know by heart pairs of multiples of 100 that make 1000.

What to do: Explain to the children what the sheet is about – adding hundreds together to make 1000 – and then let them work through it. Advise them to read carefully the information in the problems.

Differentiation: Less able children should work in a small group and they may need assistance with understanding the problems.

Extension: Children need to know by heart the pairs of multiples of 100 that total 1000, so a good homework task would be writing down the combinations and then learning them.

Add it up! Write it down! (page 74)

Objective: To develop pencil and paper methods for addition.

What to do: This method of addition will require some introduction and practice and children should not tackle the activity without them. Work through a number of similar examples together. Show the children how the working out might be written. In particular, explain the use of the brackets that they may not be familiar with.

Go through the first example on the sheet and then let the children work through the rest in the same way. The logical setting down of the thought process is as important as the correct answer, so look for sound reasoning.

Differentiation: Ask more able children to check their answers using a mental method. Less able children should tackle the sheet co-operatively in pairs or a small group.

Extension: Lots of practice is needed, so provide many similar examples, grading the difficulty according to the children's ability. More able children can begin to record the working out vertically, lining up the units and the tens and abbreviating the setting down. Thus 56 + 32 = (50 + 30) + (6 + 2) = 80 + 8 = 88 can also be written as

$$
\begin{array}{r}
56 \\
+\ 32 \\
\hline
80 \\
8 \\
=\ 88
\end{array}
$$

Zigzags (page 75)

Objective: To develop pencil and paper methods for subtraction.

What to do: The way of teaching pencil and paper methods for addition in 'Add it up! Write it down!', above, also applies here. You need to ensure that the method is fully understood before the children work on the sheet. Again, this is only a beginning and more examples need to be provided as extension work. Setting down can be gradually improved in a similar way to that suggested for the previous sheet, for example (decomposition):

$$
\begin{array}{rcccccc}
95 & & 90 & + & 5 & = & 80 & + & 15 \\
-\ 68 & & 60 & + & 8 & = & 60 & + & 8 \\
\hline
& & & & & & 20 & + & 7 & = & 27
\end{array}
$$

Differentiation/extension: See the notes for 'Add it up! Write it down', above.

Multiplying problems (page 76)

Objectives: To interpret problems as multiplication calculations; to use the operation of multiplication appropriately.

What to do: Explain that each problem on the sheet involves a multiplication calculation. Ask: *What is it in the first one?* and show the children how to record the calculation, for example: 4 × 6 = .

Differentiation: Children having difficulty should be encouraged to draw the problem, for example four rows of six, or use apparatus so that they can really see the connection between multiplication and addition.

Extension: Encourage children to respond rapidly to multiplication problems by giving them plenty of practice: *5 times what is 20? What is 9 multiplied by 2? 3 times 4?* and so on.

Leftovers (page 77)

Objective: To give a whole number and remainder when one number is divided by another.

What to do: Talk through some division examples similar to those on the sheet, getting the children to work out the answers in their heads. Go through in some detail the arithmetical operation used and introduce the word *remainder*. When they work through the activity, encourage the children to make helpful jottings on the sheet.

Differentiation: Any form of apparatus will help less numerate children, so provide a peg board, counters, cubes, or small cakes and ribbon if you have them!

Extension: Develop children's mental competence with this kind of arithmetic by giving them plenty of oral practice and problems in the form $57 = 10 \times 5 + ?$ or $19 = 6 \times 3 + ?$

Puzzle page (page 78)

Objective: To choose and use appropriate number operations to solve problems.

What to do: The only preparation that should be needed for this activity is to confirm that the children know and understand the terms *sum* and *product*. The answers are: add, divide, add, subtract, multiply; (2, 2), (6, 3), (10, 6), (4, 3), (10, 10); 1 + 6 + 2, 2 + 4 + 3 and 3 + 5 + 1.

Differentiation: Encourage the use of pencil and paper jotting so that children 'think out loud'. Allow less confident children to work co-operatively.

Extension: Challenge children to find an arrangement of the last triangular problem that requires the sum of each side to total 11 rather than 9. (4, 5, 2, 3, 6, 1, 4 in rotation.)

Taking readings
(page 79)

Objective: To read and interpret number scales.

What to do: The children will need

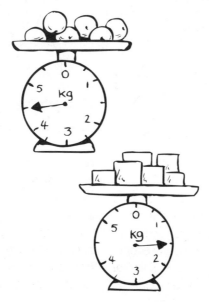

to have had some practice at reading the sort of measures shown and understand the different units of measurement before they try this activity. Note that you may want to have the option of several ways of recording the time, for example *10.25* or *25 past 10* and so on.

Differentiation: Confident children should manage without reference to apparatus, but for less able children, you should turn this into a practical exercise. Fill similar measuring jugs to the levels given, set up clocks and weighing scales in the same way. NB: try to ensure that the clocks' hands are geared properly, some cheap cardboard clock faces do not show the proper movement of the hour hand. Compensate for this or use real clocks.

Extension: Give lots more practice at reading measures. Move the positions of the hands, markers and levels on the sheet and reuse. This could be given as a task to be completed at home.

Shaping up (page 80)

Objective: To describe and classify common 2-D shapes according to their properties.

What to do: Explain to the children that you want them to draw connecting lines from the description on the left of the sheet to the shape on the right that matches it. Stress that each statement is exclusive to a particular shape.

Differentiation: Let less able children work in pairs and give them selections of shapes to handle and match to the statements. (You can make your own, but there are suitable plastic and card shapes available from many educational equipment suppliers.)

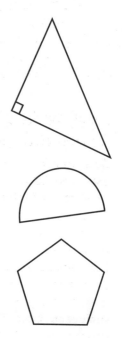

Extension: Ask children to name the shapes on the sheet. Get them to sort collections of 2-D shapes according to chosen criteria, for example quadrilaterals and not quadrilaterals.

Lines of symmetry
(page 81)

Objective: To recognise lines of symmetry in simple cases.

What to do: This is a good activity to follow up work that has been done on symmetry. The children will need to be made aware that sometimes there is more than one line of symmetry. Can they spot any shapes here that have more than one? (For example, the Union Jack.) Ideally, the children should use pencils and rulers to draw the lines.

Differentiation: Small plastic mirrors can be used to find the lines of symmetry. Put less able children in a group and show them how this can be done. All the children might check their answers in this way.

Extension: You could supply an assortment of 2-D shapes for the children to play with. Can they find any shapes with no lines of symmetry? One only? Two? More than two? A mirror can be used again here to help their exploration.

Mirror image

(page 82)

Objective: To sketch the reflection of a simple 2-D shape on a mirror line along one edge.

What to do: This sheet is self-explanatory. You might want to demonstrate the use of a mirror in this way beforehand, but it is preferable to let the children explore this for themselves. Working in pairs may stimulate discussion and ideas.

Differentiation: The activity can be simplified by getting children to draw over the lines with coloured chalk or other suitable medium; then they can fold and make a 'blot' reflection.

Extension: The sheet could be enlarged and used for a painting or drawing lesson focusing on symmetry.

Where are they? (page 83)

Objective: To describe positions on a grid.

What to do: Play 'Noughts and crosses' or 'Battleships' – any game that will get the children used to the notion of positions on a grid. Teach the 'x first, y second' convention. (You could say: *We go into the house first before we go up the stairs.*)

Differentiation: It may help if, as each position is examined, children colour the square a particular colour.

Extension: Play a variation of 'Tic-tac-toe' with the children, where four in a row wins. Divide the class into two groups (by gender or shoe size, for example). Any 'address' given by a child, for example D4, is marked on the grid, but if it is given incorrectly – in the form yx instead of xy (4D instead of D4, for instance), then the team misses a go.

Right angle test

(page 84)

Objective: To use a rough template to identify or measure right angles.

What to do: Help the children to make their own right angle tester, following the instructions on the photocopiable sheet. This can be done using any scrap of paper (it is best demonstrated using a piece that has no straight edges). Show how folding the paper in half creates one straight edge. Folding again along the line of the first fold will create a right angle. Some children will find matching the straight edge, when folding, to be a challenging task. Demonstrate how this right angle that they have made can be used to test the angles presented on the sheet. Ask the children to record their answers on the sheet.

Differentiation: The initial problem is likely to be in the folding, so let groups of children use the assistance of an adult to complete this part successfully. You could provide ready-made right angles, but this would be less interesting and lose the helpful 'hands-on' element of the learning.

Extension: Let the children explore the classroom to find as many right angles as they can. Why are there so many right angles? Ask them to consider what would happen, for example, if the door had not been made with right-angled corners.

Keeping count

In ones

- Fill in the gaps on this number line.

				145	146	147	148		

- Count **on** 8 from…

200 ➡ ☐   136 ➡ ☐   71 ➡ ☐   252 ➡ ☐

- Count **back** 13 from…

140 ➡ ☐   167 ➡ ☐   216 ➡ ☐   331 ➡ ☐

In tens

1	2	3	4	5	6	7	8	9	10
11	12	13	14	15	16	17	18	19	20
21	22	23	24	25	26	27	28	29	30
31	32	33	34	35	36	37	38	39	40
41	42	43	44	45	46	47	48	49	50
51	52	53	54	55	56	57	58	59	60
61	62	63	64	65	66	67	68	69	70
71	72	73	74	75	76	77	78	79	80
81	82	83	84	85	86	87	88	89	90
91	92	93	94	95	96	97	98	99	100

- Count **on** in tens…   starting with 10. Colour the squares.
                            starting with 3. Colour the squares.
- Count **back** in tens…   starting with 98. Colour the squares.
                            starting with 91. Colour the squares.

Big steps

● Make the next steps.

153 · 163 · 173

122 · 222 · 322

600 · 500 · 400

135 · 125 · 115

1560

1460

1360

● Complete the number ladder.

1. What number will the top step be?

2. What number is the fifth step?

Getting even

● Starting with 2, colour all the even numbers.

1	2	3	4	5	6	7	8	9	10
11	12	13	14	15	16	17	18	19	20
21	22	23	24	25	26	27	28	29	30
31	32	33	34	35	36	37	38	39	40
41	42	43	44	45	46	47	48	49	50
51	52	53	54	55	56	57	58	59	60
61	62	63	64	65	66	67	68	69	70
71	72	73	74	75	76	77	78	79	80
81	82	83	84	85	86	87	88	89	90
91	92	93	94	95	96	97	98	99	100

● Complete these sentences.

Even numbers end in ☐ , ☐ , ☐ , ☐ , or ☐ .

Odd numbers end in ☐ , ☐ , ☐ , ☐ , or ☐ .

● Choose two even numbers from the 100 square. Add them. Is your answer

even or odd? _____

● Repeat with two more even numbers. Is your answer even or odd? _____

PHOTOCOPIABLE

MATHS

The missing thinks

- Complete these sequences.
- Write down the rule for each one.

5   10   15   25

_____

4   7   10   19

_____

58   56   54

_____

1   11   16   26

_____

39   35   27   23

_____

Multiples

Two four six eight
I saw a pixie on a gate.

● Lightly colour all the multiples of 2.

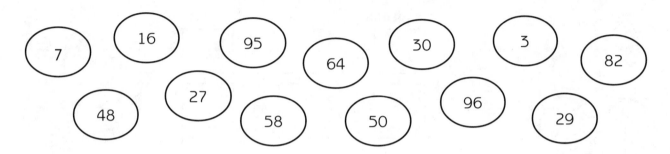

7 16 95 30 3 64 82 48 27 58 50 96 29

Five ten fifteen twenty
I think one meal a day is plenty.

● Colour in the multiples of 5.

15 22 90 31 63 50 35 70 88 54 45

● Write three multiples of 100. _____ _____ _____

● Write three multiples of 50. _____ _____ _____

● Write three multiples of 5. _____ _____ _____

● Multiples of 50 end in [   ] or [   ].

Boxed in

		H		**T**		**U**
457	is	4	and	5	and	7

457 = 400 + 50 + 7

● Let these numbers out of their boxes into…

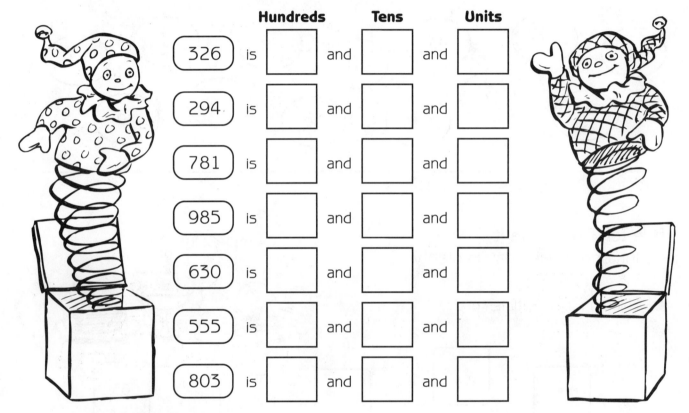

		Hundreds		**Tens**		**Units**
326	is		and		and	
294	is		and		and	
781	is		and		and	
985	is		and		and	
630	is		and		and	
555	is		and		and	
803	is		and		and	

● Complete these number sentences.

432 = ☐ + 30 + 2

697 = 600 + ☐ + 7

785 = 700 + 80 + ☐

831 = 800 + 30 + ☐

249 = 200 + ☐ + 9

More or less?

● Which is more? _____

● Which is less? _____

● Which is more: 581 or 815? _____

● Which is less: 361 or 163? _____

● Which is more? _____

Nell has 36 oranges.

Gwyn has 24 oranges.

● Who has fewer oranges? _____

● How many more oranges has Nell than Gwyn? _____

SCHOLASTIC

Piggy in the middle

What number is halfway between these?

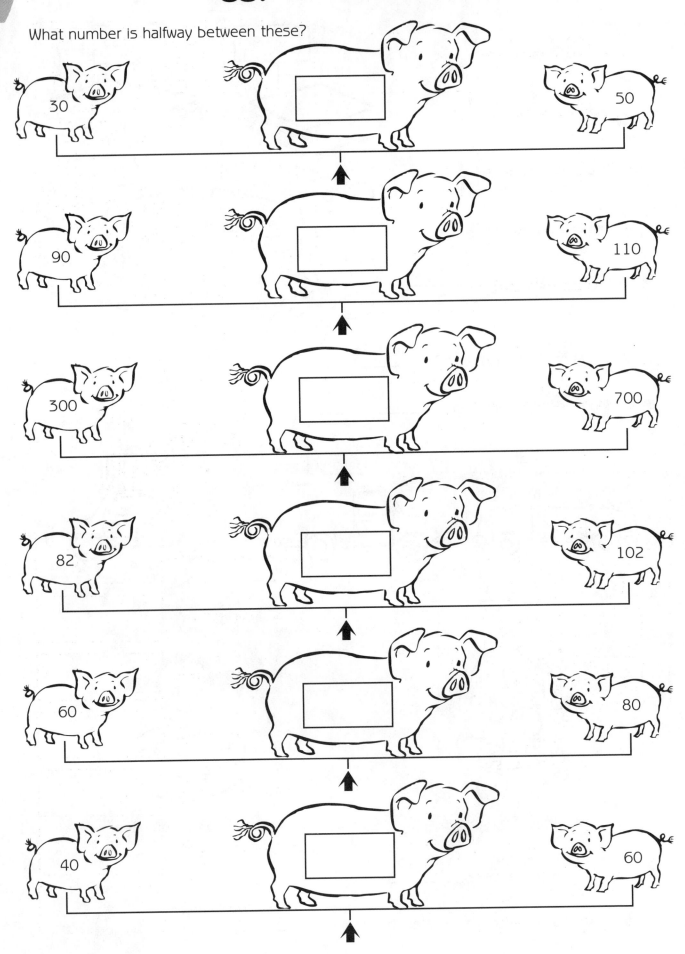

One hundred more or less

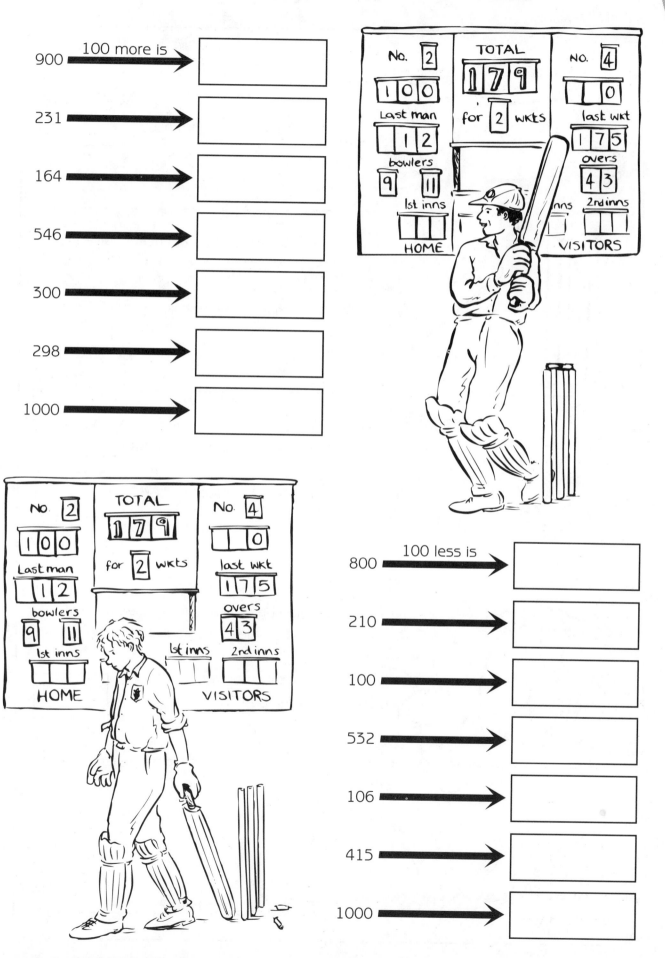

900 → 100 more is → [ ]

231 → [ ]

164 → [ ]

546 → [ ]

300 → [ ]

298 → [ ]

1000 → [ ]

800 → 100 less is → [ ]

210 → [ ]

100 → [ ]

532 → [ ]

106 → [ ]

415 → [ ]

1000 → [ ]

More or less: problems

Emma has 45p. Sam has 10p less than Emma.

How much does Sam have?

Ravi scores 9 runs at cricket. Ollie scores 100 more than Ravi.

How many runs did Ollie score?

Rose cycles 975 metres to school. Brian cycles 100 metres less than Rose.

How far does Brian cycle?

Julian buys 17kg of potatoes. Amma buys 1kg less than Julian.

How many potatoes does Amma buy?

Farmer Jones keeps 286 sheep on his farm. Farmer Williams keeps 100 more than Farmer Jones.

How many sheep does Farmer Williams keep?

Keeping order

● Put these in order – smallest first.

| 5kg | 26kg | 2kg | 63kg | 11kg |

| 323km | 451km | 167km | 28km | 204km |

Glasgow 35m
Stirling 46m

| £7.43 | £8.51 | £1.50 | £2.45 | £5.62 |

| 45cm | 31cm | 86cm | 2cm | 91cm |

| 157 | 568 | 432 | 201 | 742 |

● Fill in the missing numbers.

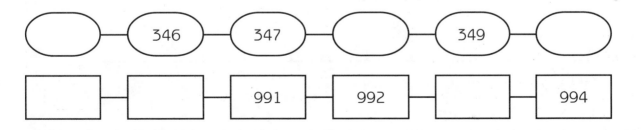

| | 346 | 347 | | 349 | |

| | | 991 | 992 | | 994 |

PHOTOCOPIABLE

MATHS

Points on a line

● Mark where you think these numbers would go on the number line.

| 36 | 51 | 10 | 88 |

0   100

● Look closely at these lines. Estimate the numbers that the arrows are pointing to.

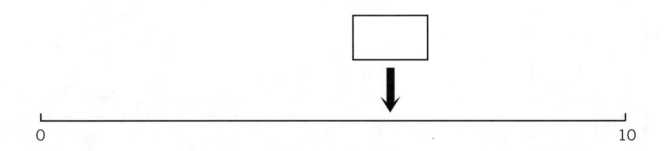

0   10

0   100

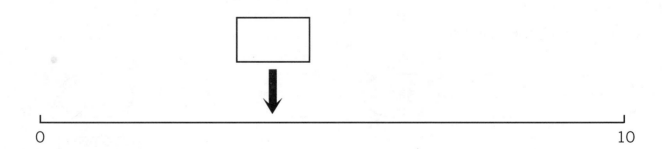

0   10

To the nearest 10

Round these numbers to the nearest 10. You could use the number lines and arrows to help you. When a number is halfway, we round up. For example, 35 rounded up to the nearest 10 is 40.

67 to the nearest 10 is _____

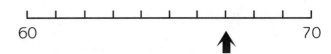

83 to the nearest 10 is _____

95 to the nearest 10 is _____

18 to the nearest 10 is _____

31 to the nearest 10 is _____

76 to the nearest 10 is _____

45 to the nearest 10 is _____

54 to the nearest 10 is _____

◢SCHOLASTIC

To the nearest 100

Round these numbers to the nearest 100. Remember to round up any numbers that are halfway between one 100 and another. For example, 150 rounded to the nearest 100 is 200.

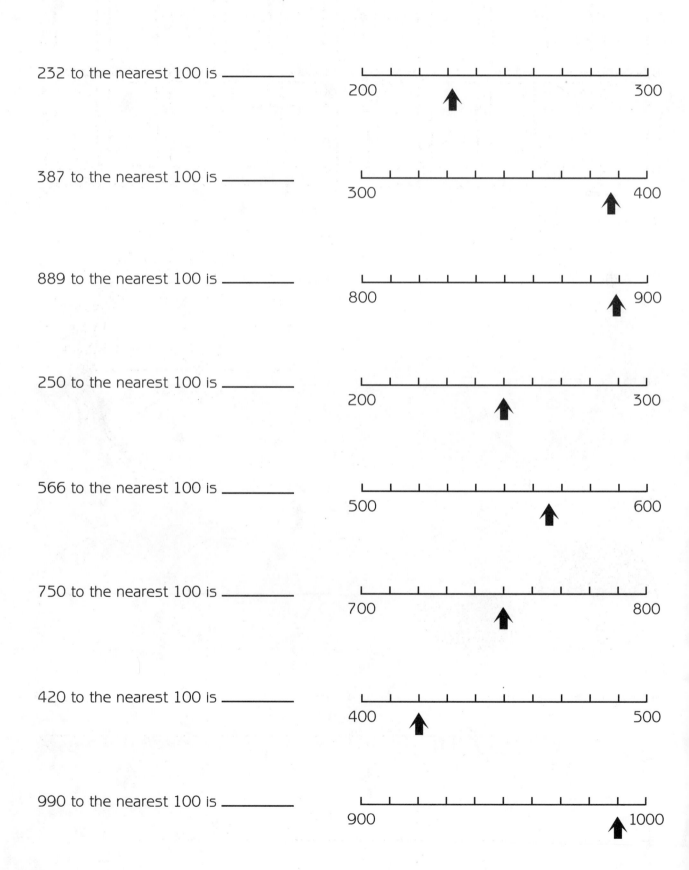

232 to the nearest 100 is _____

200   300

387 to the nearest 100 is _____

300   400

889 to the nearest 100 is _____

800   900

250 to the nearest 100 is _____

200   300

566 to the nearest 100 is _____

500   600

750 to the nearest 100 is _____

700   800

420 to the nearest 100 is _____

400   500

990 to the nearest 100 is _____

900   1000

Shady fractions

● Shade $\frac{1}{2}$ of this chocolate bar.

● Shade $\frac{1}{10}$ of this chocolate bar.

● Shade $\frac{1}{10}$ of this cake.

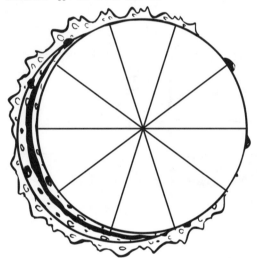

● Shade $\frac{1}{2}$ of this cake.

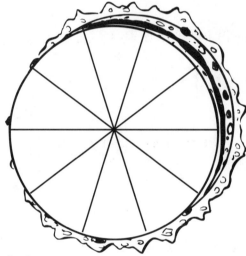

● Finish the shading until $\frac{1}{2}$ of the pattern is shaded.

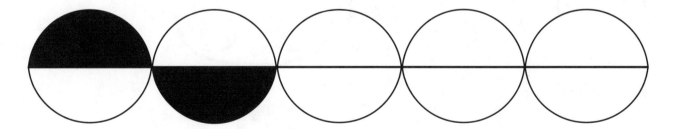

● Shade $\frac{1}{10}$ of this pattern.

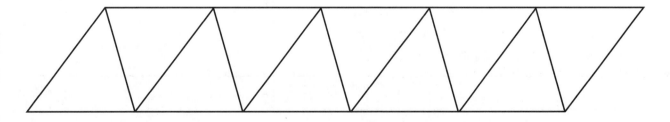

SCHOLASTIC   **67**

Finding fractions

● What fraction is shaded?

_____

● What fraction of these eggs is circled?

_____

● What fraction of these cups is circled?

_____

● What fraction of these bottles is circled?

_____

● What fraction is shaded?

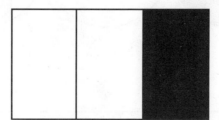

_____

● Colour $\frac{1}{4}$ of these squares red and $\frac{1}{10}$ green.

Working out fractions

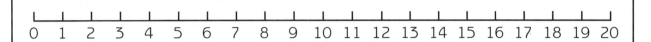

```
├──┼──┼──┼──┼──┼──┼──┼──┼──┼──┼──┼──┼──┼──┼──┼──┼──┼──┼──┼──┤
0  1  2  3  4  5  6  7  8  9  10 11 12 13 14 15 16 17 18 19 20
```

● On the number line above, what number is $\frac{1}{2}$ way? _____

● What number is $\frac{1}{4}$ of the way? _____

● What number is $\frac{3}{4}$ of the way? _____

● What number is $\frac{1}{10}$ of the way? _____

● What number is halfway between 8 and 9? _____

● What is halfway between 16 and 17? _____

● What is halfway between $1\frac{1}{2}$ and 2? _____

● What is halfway between $9\frac{1}{2}$ and 10? _____

● Estimate the fraction…

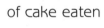 of jam in the jar   of cake eaten    of chocolates left

      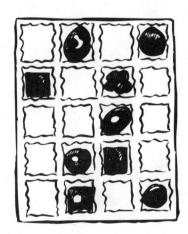

_____   _____   _____

Sum totals

● Use a number line to find two numbers that add up to 100.

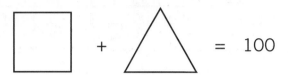

● Can you find five more pairs?

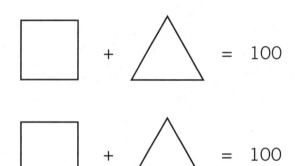

● Choose three of these numbers. Add them. _____

● How many different answers can you get, choosing three numbers each time?

Meaty sums

- Write a shopping bill of any three items.

_____

_____

_____

How much did you spend? [ ]

- Choose three different items that will cost **less** in total.

_____   _____   _____

- Choose three different items that will cost **more** in total.

_____   _____   _____

Double trouble

$1 + 1 =$

$20 + 20 =$

● Use the facts above to help you find these doubles.

$19 + 19 =$ $17 + 17 =$

$18 + 18 =$ $16 + 16 =$

● Work out the answers to these in your head.

$85 + 85 =$

$65 + 65 =$

$80 + 80 =$

$70 + 70 =$

$75 + 75 =$

● Can you explain how you did it?

Hundreds that make a thousand

● Fill in the blanks and make 1000.

500 + 500 = [ ]

200 + [ ] = 1000

[ ] + 600 = 1000

300 + [ ] = 1000

100 + 900 = [ ]

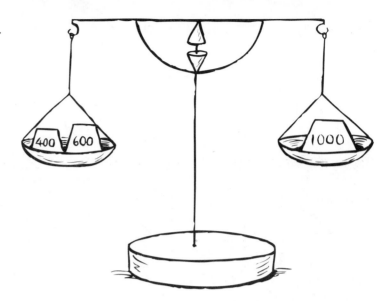

● Mr Khan travels 1000 miles in two days. On the first day he travels 600 miles. How many miles does he travel on the second day? _____

● Mrs Jones wants to buy a car. It costs £1000. She has £800. How much more money does she need? _____

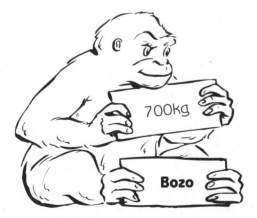

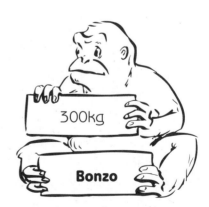

● Bozo weighs 700kg. Bonzo weighs 300kg. How much do they weigh altogether? _____

Add it up! Write it down!

Add up these numbers. Write down your working out, as shown in the example.

$56 + 32 =$ $(50 + 30) + (6 + 2) = 80 + 8 = 88$

$47 + 51 =$ ( ) + ( ) =

$63 + 26 =$ ( ) + ( ) =

$28 + 71 =$ ( ) + ( ) =

$65 + 34 =$ ( ) + ( ) =

I'm a good adder.

$68 + 27 =$

$36 + 45 =$

$77 + 19 =$

$62 + 57 =$

$85 + 64 =$

Zigzags

$95 - 68 =$ ☐ 27

Start at **68**   Add

68 → **2**

70 ←

→ **20**

90 ←

→ **5**

Got there! **95** ←

27

$81 - 57 =$ ☐

Start at   Add

$58 - 29 =$ ☐

Start at   Add

$74 - 36 =$ ☐

Start at   Add

$85 - 56 =$ ☐

Start at   Add

$62 - 45 =$ ☐

Start at   Add

Multiplying problems

● Choco Cheryl ate a whole box of chocolates. There were 4 rows of 6. How many chocolates did she eat?

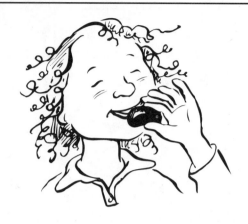

_____

● CD Sid collects CDs. He has 5 shelves with 10 on each shelf. How many CDs does he have altogether?

_____

● Mick the milkman delivers 3 bottles to every house in Sago Street. There are 7 houses in the street. How many bottles does he deliver?

_____

● Sara Stalk has 3 times as many roses as Rose Red. Rose has 8 roses. How many does Sara have?

_____

Leftovers

● 18 small cakes are shared between 5 people. How many are left over?

● A roll of ribbon 92cm long is cut into 10cm strips. How many strips are cut? How much is left?

● What is the remainder when 17 is divided by 3?

| 35 ÷ 10 = 3 remainder 5 |

● Work out:

67 ÷ 10 =

42 ÷ 10 =

99 ÷ 10 =

● Each taxi can carry 4 passengers. How many taxis would be needed for 22 passengers?

Puzzle page

● What does ⭐ stand for in these calculations?

9 ⭐ 7 = 16 _____

35 ⭐ 5 = 7 _____

43 ⭐ 78 = 121 _____

170 ⭐ 32 = 138 _____

16 ⭐ 10 = 160 _____

● Find a pair of numbers with:

a sum of 4 and a product of 4 _____

a sum of 9 and a product of 18 _____

a sum of 16 and a product of 60 _____

a sum of 7 and a product of 12 _____

a sum of 20 and a product of 100 _____

● Place all of the numbers 1, 2, 3, 4, 5 and 6 to make each side of this triangle total 9.

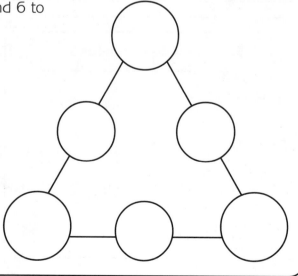

Taking readings

Write down the measures shown.

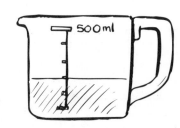

_____

_____

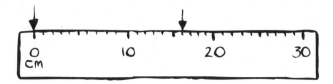

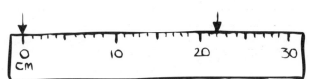

_____

_____

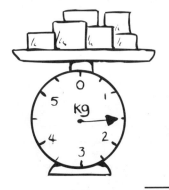

_____

_____

_____

_____

Shaping up

Connect each shape to its correct description.

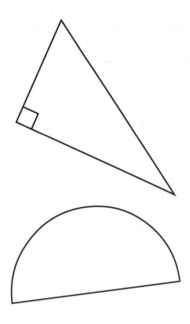

Has four equal sides and four right angles

A triangle without a right angle

Has five equal sides and angles

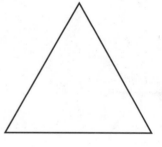

Half a circle

A triangle with a right angle

Has four right angles. Not all the sides are the same length, but opposite sides are equal.

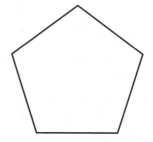

Lines of symmetry

● Draw the lines of symmetry on these shapes.

● Do any have more than one? Do any have none at all?

Mirror image

Complete the picture. Use a mirror to help.

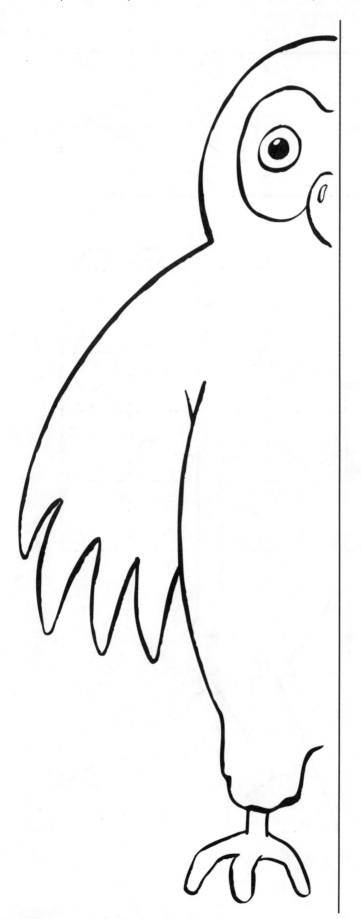

Where are they?

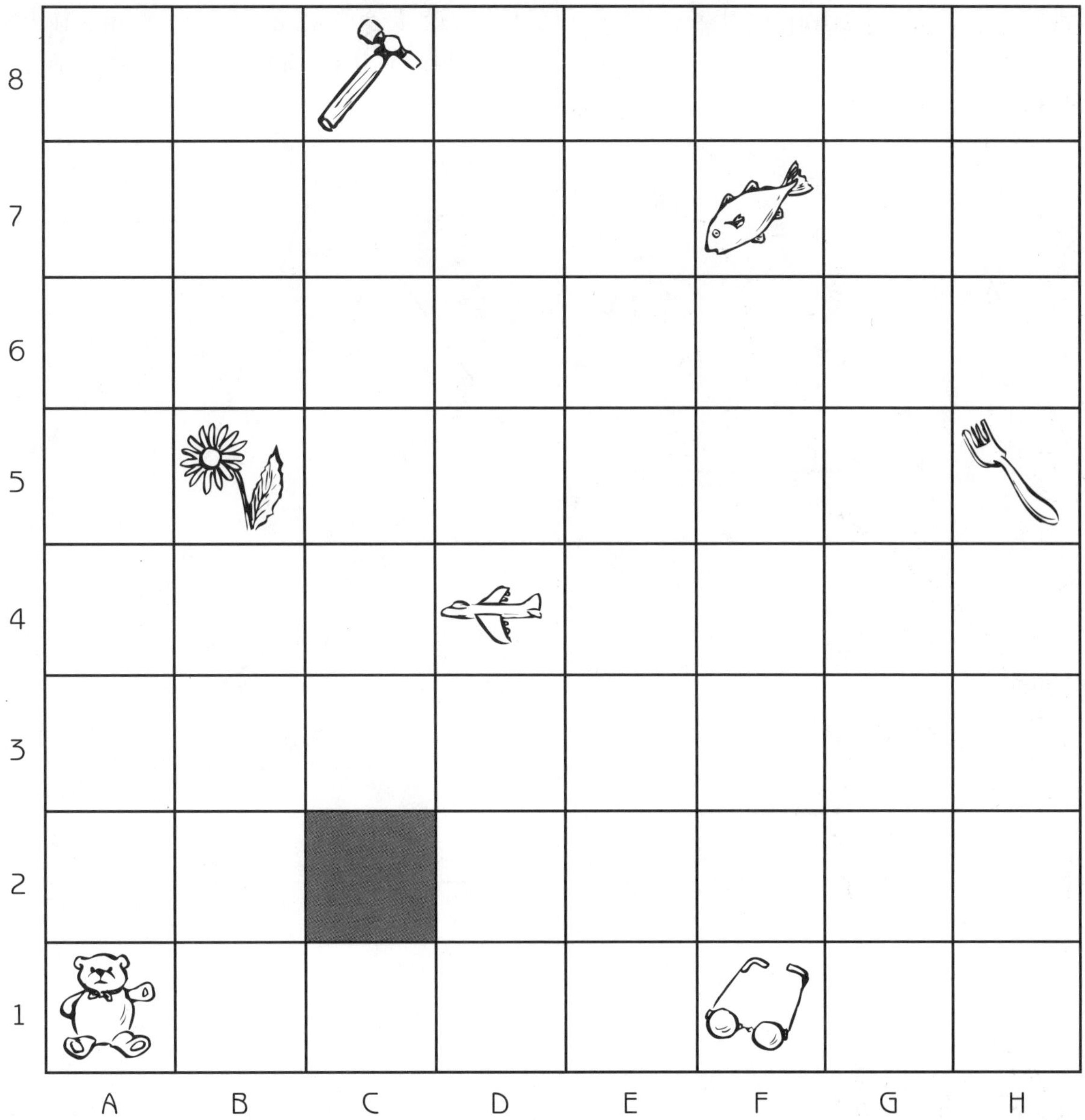

The shaded square is | C2 |

Where is...?

the aeroplane [ ]   the bear [ ]   the hammer [ ]

the pair of spectacles [ ]   the fork [ ]   the fish [ ]

the flower [ ]

PHOTOCOPIABLE

MATHS

Right angle test

Tear a strip from the bottom of this sheet. Fold it in half, then half again to make a right angle tester. Use it to say which of these angles is **more** or **less** than a right angle. Are any of them right angles?

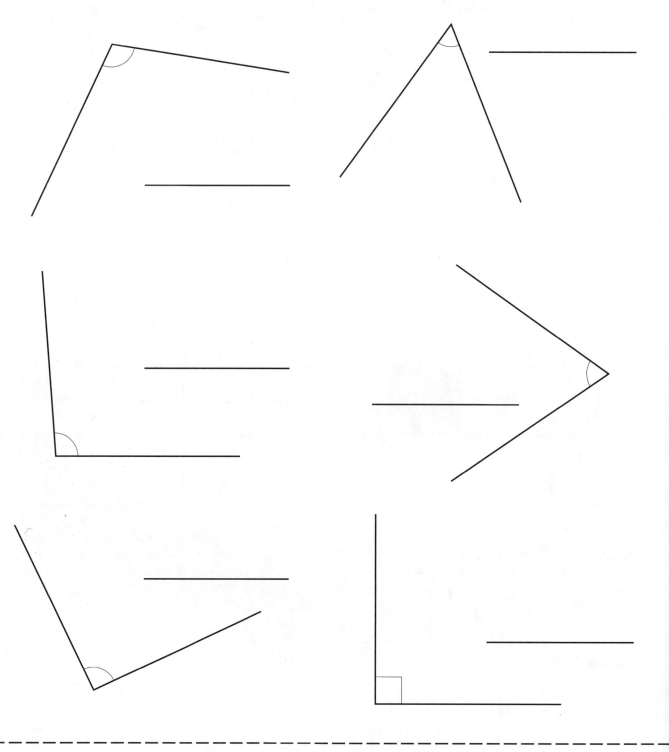

SCIENCE

It would be misleading to say that real science begins in Year 3, but it can feel like it, for it is at this stage that the National Curriculum requirements for children to collect evidence, test predictions, draw conclusions and make sure that evidence is sufficient to support conclusions become particularly conspicuous. In Year 3, classroom experimentation begins to resemble the sort of science that a child's grandparents might recognise. Encouraging and exciting though this is, the approach poses problems when it comes to devising and using worksheets. We have set down only a few 'experiments' for children to follow from the sheets because we do not feel that this is the way to introduce such work at this age. We have, however, made the assumption that the activities will be set firmly in the context of observation and experiment. The sheets broadly fit the content suggested in the QCA scheme of work and, within it, those objectives that worksheets are best able to support.

The National Curriculum science contexts are 'Life processes and living things', 'Materials and their properties' and 'Physical processes'. 'Scientific enquiry' (Sc1), sets out the skills and principles to be taught through these contexts. For Year 3, QCA propose six units covered in a total curriculum time of 65 hours, six more hours than in Year 2. The units are 'Teeth and eating', 'Helping plants grow well', 'Characteristics of materials', 'Rocks and soils', 'Magnets and springs', 'Light and shadows'. The worksheets in this book follow progressively from those in volumes for the preceding year groups, so differentiated work can be created easily using material prepared for other years.

A varied diet (page 89)

Objective: To understand that an adequate and healthy diet is needed for growth and activity.

What to do: The sheet shows simplified concepts that will be built on by later learning. For example, protein is the main body builder, but it can also provide the body with energy if the diet does not include enough carbohydrates and fats. Children need to be introduced to the vocabulary and ways of recognising different food types before they can attempt this activity. Make sure that *diet* is understood not just in the narrow sense of 'reduced food intake for the purpose of losing weight'.

Differentiation: Provide reference books, a wordbank, picture bank or other display in the classroom to which children can refer. This will assist less able children in identifying the categories of food.

Extension: Using these food categories, analyse the school meals menu for a week.

The truth about teeth (page 90)

Objective: To learn about the different types of teeth and their functions.

What to do: Take out your teeth (the model ones the school has for this purpose, of course!) and let the children examine, discuss and name the types of teeth. The school health service or a local dentist may be able to assist here. Ask the children to number the illustrations on the sheet according to the descriptions given. The puzzle answers are: across 1. milk, 3. decay, 5. molars, 6. gums; down 2. incisors, 4. canines.

Differentiation: Some children will require longer to get to grips with the terminology, so allow them more time to examine and discuss the types of teeth. Let them work in pairs.

Extension: You should take the opportunity to extend this work into the area of dental hygiene and this is best achieved by employing the expertise of a health professional, such as the school nurse or dentist. At some point, children should examine their own teeth.

Tooth decay (page 91)

Objective: To understand that some foods damage the health of teeth by causing decay.

What to do: Understanding diagrams like this can be difficult for young children and you should take time to explain what is happening, ideally with reference to a set of teeth. Tell the children that they should explain the stages of decay in simple terms, following on from the introduction on the sheet. Ask them to include reference to bad eating habits (such as too many sweets); possibly bad hygiene (lack of teeth brushing); and a simple explanation of how bacteria can cause decay and the loss of a tooth. Try to be positive when referring to dental work – it is as much about prevention as repair.

Differentiation: Let less able children simply focus on describing why teeth decay. Covering the diagram may simplify matters.

Extension: There are a number of poems about teeth (from Pam Ayres to Spike Milligan) that will amuse the children. Read some together, then ask the class to write a poem describing the horrible fate of Nelly who neglected her teeth. Alternatively, set groups of children to write rules for looking after your teeth or exploring what happens when a child loses a milk tooth.

Tooth damage (page 92)

Objective: To identify particular foods as damaging to teeth and others as less damaging.

What to do: Make sure the children understand the notions of *damaging* and *less damaging*. Teeth need healthy gums and some foods can be particularly damaging, especially where there is not a strict regime of teeth cleaning, but don't give children a complex about this or they will be too frightened to eat their crème brulée! The foods pictured should be linked to the appropriate set using a line, or the names of the foods can be written into the sets. Encourage the children to add more foods to the sets.

Differentiation: Some children will benefit from undertaking this activity co-operatively, if necessary with an adult on hand to assist the discussion.

Extension: Undertake a 'hunt the sugar' investigation. Ask the children to examine the ingredients listed on packages and tins looking for the word *sugar*. How many packaged foods have sugar added to them? There may be some surprises. This would be an interesting homework task.

Growing well? How can we tell?

(page 93)

Objective: To ask questions about the growth of plants.

What to do: This sheet is no substitute for experiment and observation, but can be used to confirm learning after children have been working with plants. From their observations and after studying the illustrations, ask them to complete the chart, making comments on each part of the plant in turn.

Differentiation: Where children experience difficulty, using the sheet in conjunction with the observation of real plants should help.

Extension: Set up some simple experiments for the children to carry out. By measuring, comparing, and controlling the growth of similar plants in different circumstances (such as water/no water, light/shade, removing/not removing dead leaves) children can ascertain plants' requirements for good growth.

Celery science (page 94)

Objective: To ask questions about the growth of plants.

What to do: This activity requires children to set up and perform a simple experiment, so you will need the apparatus shown on the sheet. Use a stick of celery with the root removed but with some of the leaves retained. This is a simple experiment that encourages children to observe carefully and record what they see. The pictures should record what the children observe:

1. when first putting the celery in the coloured water
2. as the water rises
3. when the experiment stabilises.

The children might include vocabulary such as *drawn, stem, roots* and *plant* in their statement describing the results.

Differentiation: Less able children should work in a well-controlled environment with an adult on hand to assist when there are problems.

Extension: There are all sorts of simple experiments that children can do using growing plants. Ideally, they should carry out an experiment to test the growth of plants under different watering conditions. These should involve accurate measurements of different quantities of water.

Eating the countryside (page 95)

Objective: To recognise that plants can provide food for us and that some plants are grown for this purpose.

What to do: Ask the children to examine the picture for edible plants. They should spot wheat, beans, lettuce/cabbage, apples, pears and strawberries. They may suggest others (such as the blackberries) so give them credit for having sharp eyes. When they are thinking of other edible plants, let the children include those that are not grown in this country, for example bananas as well as potatoes, carrots and mushrooms.

Differentiation: Enlarging the sheet may help those who struggle with the detail of the picture.

Extension: Use an outline map of the world and ask children to find out where foods they eat are grown. Stick labels from bags of oranges, cans of sweetcorn and so on around the map and link them to their country of origin.

Something made from... (page 96)

Objectives: To identify a range of common materials; to understand that the same material can be used to make different objects.

What to do: This sheet should be used in the context of a project on materials. You might classify materials according to terms used by the children then reduce these to the terms used on the photocopiable sheet. The answer to the final question is best given orally and is really a matter for class discussion after the sheet has been completed.

Differentiation: Give less able children Post-it Notes marked *wood, plastic, metal* and *glass* and a selected group of classroom objects on which to stick the labels. That way you can make the exercise slightly easier by controlling the objects under observation. The list of objects can be transferred to the sheet when the classification has been made.

Extension: Repeat the activity for homework, limiting the observation to objects in the children's own rooms.

Material match (page 97)

Objectives: To recognise properties of materials, such as hardness and flexibility; to understand that some materials are suitable for making a particular object because of their properties.

What to do: Introduce the term *properties*, in relation to the examples of materials given on the sheet. Ask the children to examine the list of words, then chose appropriate ones to write under the objects. Advise them that they can use more than one word and use the same word for several objects.

Differentiation: You may need to go through the word list with some children. Make sure they fully understand the meanings of the words. Encourage them to use dictionaries to help them.

Extension: Ask children to add two more words to the descriptions of each object. They could use dictionaries and a thesaurus. This would be good for homework.

Why metal? (page 98)

Objective: To recognise that materials are suitable for making particular objects because of their properties and that some properties are more important than others when deciding what to use.

What to do: Let the children chose a material from the list given and then describe what might happen if the object were made from it. The results are intended to be inappropriate – a key made of cheese? Explain to the children that they can chose one material for each object – there are enough choices for each material to be used only once. There could be advantages as well as disadvantages for certain objects. When they record, encourage the children to use adjectives from the previous activity, for example *wool is not <u>rigid</u> enough to make a dish*.

Differentiation: Put less able children in groups so that they can discuss what would happen. If writing is a problem, let them give answers orally to an adult.

Extension: Challenge children to name one or two materials that would be right to use for each object. For example, a spoon – metal, wood and plastic.

Rocks and soils (page 99)

Objective: To identify a variety of rocks and soils.

What to do: This activity looks at the properties of rocks and soils by thinking about the use we make of them. Tell the children to draw a line from each drawing on the sheet to the correct material. A statue could

be made from several materials, but the children should be able to identify marble by process of elimination at least.

Differentiation: It may help some children if you label the illustrations as *dry stone wall* and so on.

Extension: Using reference books, challenge children to list as many different rocks and soils as they can. More able children may be able to use sophisticated terms, such as *rose quartz* and *iron pyrites*.

Where are the rocks? (page 100)

Objective: To learn that beneath all land surfaces there is rock.

What to do: You may suggest that the children colour the rocks that they spot on the sheet, or use a coloured pencil to indicate with an arrow where the rocks are visible. They are not visible in the picture of fields nor in the town street. Ensure that the children understand that stones and pebbles are small pieces of rock.

Differentiation: Other than help with reading the instructions, all Year 3 children should be able to cope with this activity with little or no assistance.

Extension: Move on to examine and test the characteristics of different rocks. Assemble a collection of rocks and stones for children to order in terms of resistance to wear. Help them to devise a fair test to see which rocks produce small particles most readily when rubbed.

Natural attraction (page 101)

Objective: To make and test predictions about whether materials are magnetic or not.

What to do: It is most important that the children make predictions before testing. Collect the common objects listed on the sheet and ask the children to make their predictions on magnetism by putting the object in the category where they think it would fit. They will then need a magnet to test their predictions, writing their test results down in the other table. Have a class discussion about the accuracy of the predictions. What conclusions can the children draw from their tests? (All objects attracted to magnets are made of metal, but not all objects that are made of metal are attracted to magnets. Iron, steel, nickel and cobalt and objects containing these metals are attracted to magnets, no others.)

Differentiation: You may think it appropriate to limit the number of objects tested by some children and to exclude the pins and scissors from the test for any children who may not cope safely with them.

Extension: What use are magnets? Set this problem for a bit of classroom research or homework. Can the children find out about one piece of equipment in which they are used?

Springs (page 102)

Objective: To understand that springs are used in a variety of ways.

What to do: Make sure first of all that everyone knows what a spring is. The children could practise drawing them. Ask them to circle or draw arrows to indicate where they think the springs are used in the objects on the sheet. Each one needs at least one spring in order to function. (Point out, if necessary, that the pen is retractable.) To help the children with the last question, provide them with access to suitable reference books or CD-ROMs.

Differentiation: Hands-on experience is the best support for those having difficulty. The smaller objects can be examined in the classroom; you might be able to examine an old armchair instead of the bed; the springs in the suspension are usually accessible to viewing in most cars.

Extension: Set children on a spring hunt. How many uses for springs can they find in their own home?

Which way? (page 103)

Objective: To understand that forces act in particular directions.

What to do: This activity tests the children's understanding of directional force and of forces working in opposite directions. Check their understanding of pushes and pulls. Suggest that they use a different coloured arrow for each illustration on the sheet.

Differentiation: Each illustration can be treated as an experiment for replication if the children need help.

Extension: Many of the children will own skates or skateboards. Let them draw themselves (cartoon style) propelling themselves or being propelled in a particular way. Ask them to indicate the direction of movement in the same way as on the photocopiable sheet.

OTT (page 104)

Objective: To understand the properties *opaque*, *translucent* and *transparent* and how they are defined in terms of the transmission of light.

What to do: Explain to the children that they have to decide whether the object on the sheet does not let through any light (opaque), lets some light through (translucent), or lets lots of light through so that objects can clearly be seen through it (transparent). Children tend to enjoy using these words, so encourage them.

The mirror is a bit of a trick question. It is, of course, opaque, but does *reflect* light – a different concept. When they have completed the sheet, ask the children to list objects that they have classified themselves.

Differentiation: For anyone struggling with these definitions, it should be a case of seeing is believing. Under adult supervision, a small group could examine each object in turn. Try testing them for light transmission by shining a torch at them.

Extension: Link the study of shadows with the concepts on this sheet. Test objects that are opaque against objects that are transparent. Which cast the strongest shadows? (Note that even transparent objects block some light and can cast faint shadows.)

Shapely shadows (page 105)

Objectives: To understand that shadows are formed when objects block the light source and that shadows form in a similar shape to the object; to understand that the shadows of objects in sunlight change in position according to the time of day.

What to do: This sheet describes an experiment to be carried out by two children. Ask the children to record their findings and thoughts on a separate sheet. In its simplest form, the experiment can be carried out over the duration of a sunny school day. Where you opt for a series of recordings over time, perhaps comparing seasons, careful records should be kept and this is best done on a class basis. Make the results the focus of a class discussion. Children should notice that the position of the sun appears to change throughout the day. They should also see that when the sun is behind an object, the shadow is in front.

Differentiation: Less able children will need to do this experiment with adult help in order to measure and record accurately.

Extension: Ask children to investigate directions. Which way does the sun appear to move every day?

The sundial (page 106)

Objectives: To understand that shadows can be used to tell the approximate time; to make a sundial.

What to do: Making the sundial is straightforward. The tricky bit is to make reasonable calibrations against clock time. Ideally, the sundial should remain in place for accurate recording of the shadows cast.

Differentiation: Some children will need careful supervision, especially when marking the shadows' positions.

Extension: Ask children to design an advertisement for a sundial, praising its advantages and describing how it should be used.

A varied diet

We eat food so that we can grow, keep healthy and be active.

Best foods for growth

Best foods for activity

protein
milk, fish, meat, eggs, cheese, beans, nuts, peas

carbohydrates and fats
bread, potatoes, noodles, cereal, rice, sugar, pasta, butter, margarine, oil

For growth

For activity

Cut out these foods and put them in the correct set above.

The truth about teeth

We have three different types of teeth.

1. **incisors** — These have flat sides and sharp edges. Top and bottom incisors meet to cut food.

2. **canines** — These are sharp and pointed for gripping and tearing food such as meat.

3. **molars and premolars** — These have peaks or cusps that fit into hollows in the teeth opposite. They are for grinding and chewing food.

● Which is which?

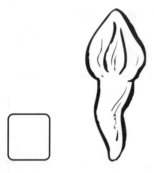 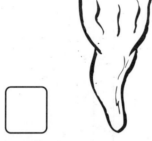 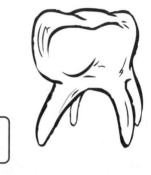

● Get your teeth into this puzzle.

Across
1. Your first teeth. Do cows make them?
3. When teeth are bad, they _____.
5. For chewing.
6. Where teeth are fixed.

Down
2. For cutting.
4. For tearing.

Tooth decay

The **enamel** that covers your teeth is very tough, but if you eat a lot of sugar, **bacteria** in your mouth feed on the sugar and produce **acid** which attacks the enamel.

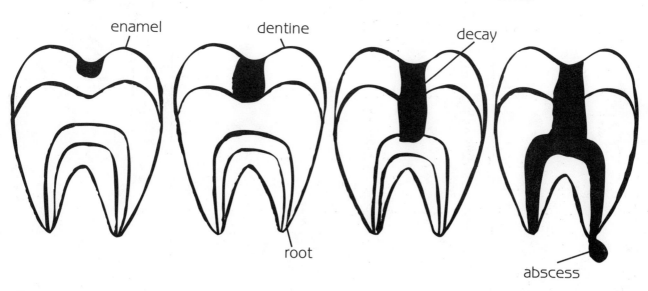

Explain what is happening here. Suggest reasons why.

Tooth damage

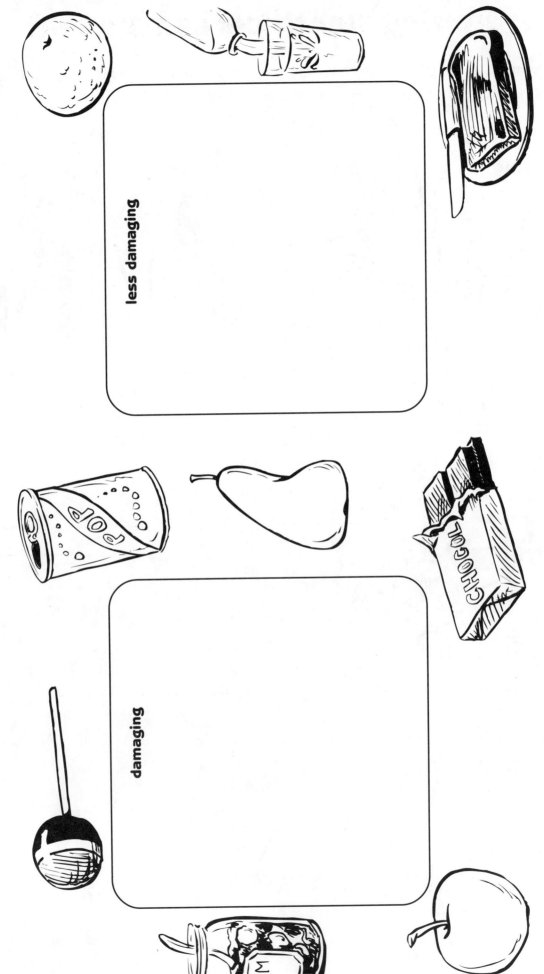

less damaging

damaging

- Link these foods to their right sets.
- Can you add any more? Draw them in the sets.

Growing well? How can we tell?

A.

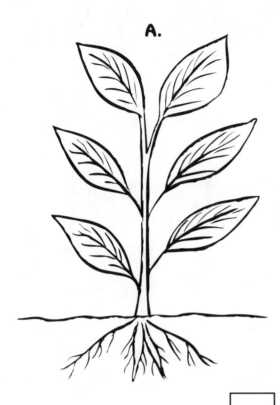

B.

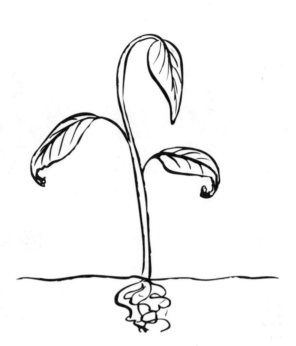

● Which plant is growing well? ☐

● Look at and comment on:

	A.	B.
the leaves		
the stem		
the roots		

📖SCHOLASTIC

Celery science

● Do this experiment. Look carefully at the head of the celery.

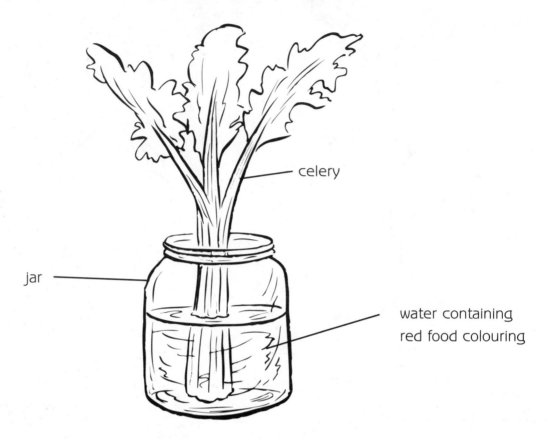

celery

jar

water containing
red food colouring

● Draw diagrams of what happens when you put the celery in the water.

1.	2.	3.

The water is _____ through the _____

to the other parts of the _____.

Eating the countryside

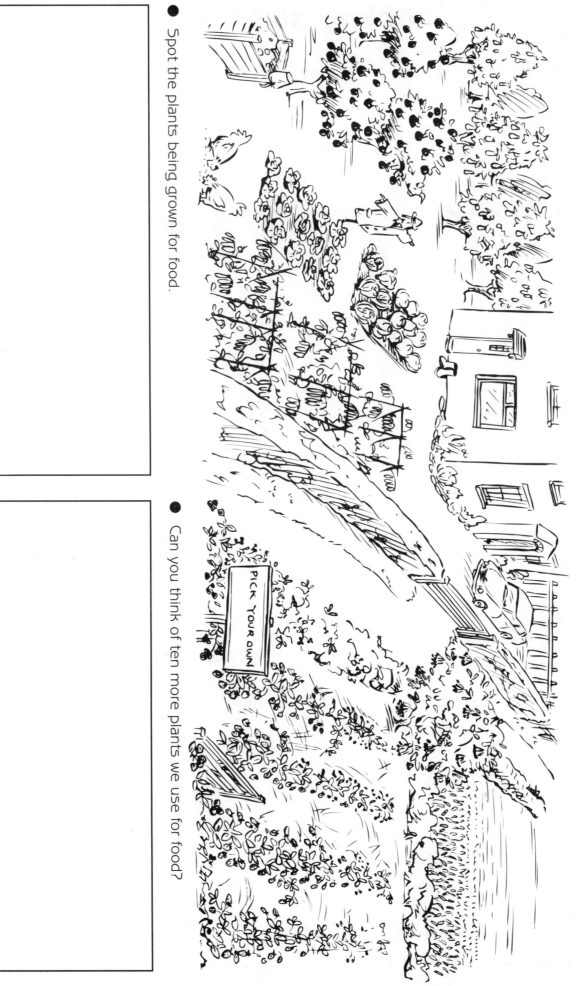

- Spot the plants being grown for food.

- Can you think of ten more plants we use for food?

Something made from...

● List all the objects you can find in the classroom made from these materials.

● How can you tell what they are made from?

Material match

Choose words from the list at the bottom of the page to describe these objects.

_____

_____

_____

_____

_____

_____

_____

_____

_____

_____

_____

_____

_____

_____

_____

_____

_____

_____

_____

_____

_____

_____

_____

_____

Properties of materials

hard	strong		shiny	cold
		smooth	dull	transparent
soft	flexible			
	rough	sharp		opaque
	rigid		stretchy	
thin		thick		absorbent

Why metal?

What would happen if these objects were made of...?

(cheese) (rubber) (plastic) (wool) (glass) (wood) (stone)

bell	
spoon	
key	
nail	
baking dish	
coin	
weight	

Rocks and soils

Link the part of the picture to its rock or soil.

chalk

clay

marble

slate

pebbles

limestone

sand

SCHOLASTIC

Where are the rocks?

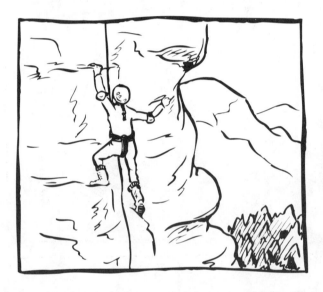

- Mark where the rocks are in these pictures.
- Why can't we see rocks in some of the pictures? Where are they?

Natural attraction

Find out which of these objects are attracted to a magnet.

pencil   paperclip   drink can   coin   stick of chalk   scissors   key

ruler   pins   eraser   glass jar   small stone   nail   spoon

Prediction (what I think will happen)	
attracted	**not attracted**

Test (what actually happens)	
attracted	**not attracted**

Springs

● Mark or write down where the springs are in these items.

● Can you think of any other uses for springs?

Which way?

Draw an arrow to show which direction the baby cart will move in.

Baby is pushed.

Baby is pulled.

Baby pushes against the wall.

Baby is pulled.

OTT

● Are these objects **opaque**, **translucent** or **transparent**?

empty milk bottle

tree

mirror

_____

_____

_____

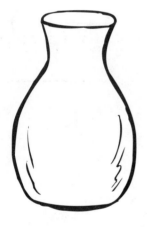

frosted glass vase

window

television

_____

_____

_____

● Can you find another object for each category?

opaque	**translucent**	**transparent**

Shapely shadows

Our bodies will not let light through them. (Things that absorb or reflect light are **opaque**.) Your shadow is the bit of ground that does not get any sunlight because your body is in the way.

Short shadows and long shadows

● Try this experiment when the Sun is shining brightly.

Stand in the same place once every hour. Ask a friend to note the position and length of your shadow each time.

● What happens to your shadow? Can you explain why?

PHOTOCOPIABLE

SCIENCE

The sundial

Over 4000 years ago, the Babylonians invented the first shadow clock, or sundial, which they used to tell the time. A gnomon – an upright piece of metal – cast a shadow on the stone surface.

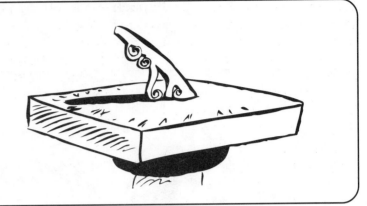

● Make your own sundial.

1. Choose a sunny spot. Turn a flowerpot upside down.

2. Put a long stick through the hole in the base of the pot and push it into the ground to make it straight and firm.

3. Every hour, use a marker pen to mark the position of the shadow cast by the stick.

You now have a sundial and can use it to tell the time.

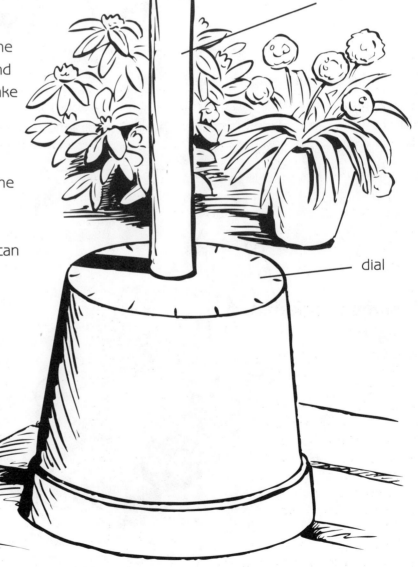

gnomon

dial

● When is your sundial no use?

HISTORY

Because six into four doesn't go precisely, apportioning the content of the history curriculum for Key Stage 2 children is open to a considerable number of variations. The six units – a local history study, three British history studies, a European history study and a world history study – do not even have to be taught discretely. A local study might also focus on an area in Tudor times, a study of education in the locality might encompass 'Victorian Britain' and 'Britain since 1930'. In practice, however, the number of curriculum variations adopted by schools has tended to be quite small, the most common pathway through the historical maze being the broadly chronological one, with Ancient Egypt the most popular world history study. This is the path we have followed here, although of course we could not include sheets to service all local history projects. We have, however, made suggestions about possible local projects where the opportunity arises.

For Year 3, we have concentrated on the waves of invaders and settlers to which Britain was subject throughout the first millennium AD – Romans, Anglo-Saxons and Vikings – as Key Stage 2 children are expected to have an overview of all these and to carry out a detailed study of one. As the curriculum need not necessarily be taught sequentially, we are aware that this topic might be taught to any Key Stage 2 year group and have therefore tried to include some more demanding work in the extension activities. These notes cannot supply sufficient background historical information, so you will need other reference material. For succinct overviews of the historical topics for Key Stage 2, see *History* in Scholastic's *Pocket Guides to the Primary Curriculum* series.

A Roman legionary

(page 111)

Objective: To begin to understand why the Romans were successful in their invasion of Britain.

What to do: Ask the children to use the information to label the diagram. The parts can be labelled using the correct Latin terms if you wish. Explain to the children that, although outnumbered, the legions were successful in Britain largely because of superior training, tactics and discipline. Legionaries were trained to fight but could do other things as well, for they were field engineers with skills in building bridges, roads and forts.

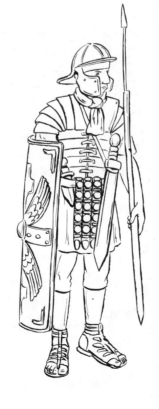

Each legion contained clerks, medical orderlies, musicians, standard bearers and all the other staff required by a small army. Overall, the Romans ultimately used about 50 000 men to subdue Britain.

Differentiation: Give help with the reading where required. More able children will enjoy learning the Latin names for the soldier's equipment. Supply reference books to support this topic.

Extension: Encourage the children to find out more about the Roman army in Britain. *What were auxiliaries? How did the Romans fight? Did they use cavalry?* Give groups of children one question to answer and report back on to the rest of the class. There is also plenty of opportunity for art and craft work. You could try making and dressing a Roman legionary.

Roman buildings in Britain

(page 112)

Objective: To find out about the effect of Roman settlement on Britain.

What to do: Reading the introduction on the sheet might be sufficient, but the children should really have been introduced to these aspects of Roman society before attempting the activity. Ask them to examine the pictures and name the buildings shown.

Differentiation: Provide plenty of reference books, CD-ROMs and so on to support this work. Ask more able children to write brief descriptions of the buildings and what they were used for. These descriptions could be in the form of captions for the pictures.

Extension: Any of the pictures can be selected and used as the focus for more extensive research work. Direct this research fairly narrowly, for example: *Find out three important facts about villas.*

Roman mosaics

(page 113)

Objective: To find out about the effect of Roman settlement on Britain.

What to do: The sheet looks at one of the legacies of Roman settlement in Britain. Discuss Roman mosaics with the class – what they were, how they were made, how we know about them, where they can be found today and so on. Using enlarged copies of the sheet, children can simply enjoy colouring in the mosaic to create an image of what it might have looked like when it was originally laid. (Early mosaics were black and white, but later ones used a number of colours including cream, yellow, red, grey and blue). The sheet can also be the starting point for the children to make a mosaic of their own. Sticky paper on card is simple, clay tesserae set in plaster a more sophisticated approach. Make sure that the children study mosaic designs first so that they understand authentic Roman designs. You could try to replicate the guilloche, but it is a complex design and there are simpler ones, such as the chequer board. Mosaics are preserved at historic sites and in museums all over Britain, but the most splendid are displayed in the British Museum in London.

Differentiation: Give less able children a section of the pattern to tackle.

Extension: A visit to a real mosaic would be fascinating, and there are some first-rate sites in Britain.

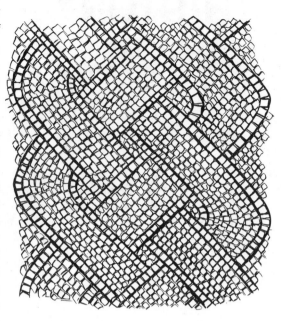

Public baths (page 114)

Objective: To understand about life in Roman Britain from a range of sources.

What to do: This text should be read out loud, perhaps as part of a whole-class lesson. To introduce it, talk about what Roman baths were like and have plenty of reference material to hand, especially pictorial. Make sure the children understand that this is a real letter (it is a précis of one sent by Seneca the Younger from his flat in Rome to his friend Lucilius). The suggested activity (interrogating this bit of evidence for information) will test children's understanding of this aspect of Roman life in an amusing way. They could design an estate agent's blurb (show them a modern example if possible) to try to sell Seneca's flat, making the proximity of the bath an advantage rather than a disadvantage. Let them draw a picture to go with their text. Explain that the baths would have a hot-air/hot-bath room, a warm-air/warm-bath room and a cold-air/cold-bath room, but the grander establishments could have associated snack bars, shops, restaurants, meeting rooms, gardens, exercise rooms, places for sports and massages and very public toilets. Baths were popular meeting places for friends to gossip, to make business contacts and so on.

Differentiation: This is a challenging literary source and therefore difficult for young children, so you might want to undertake the activity as an oral one. Read out the letter dramatically. Play the part of Seneca and allow the children to interrogate you about your letter. The children's response to the sheet could be oral and pictorial rather than written. Lots of resources should be on hand for children to refer to.

Extension: Find out what other facilities the Romans built in their towns. Ask children to design visitor's notes for someone visiting a Roman town. (If you are near a Roman site this could be based on a real one.) The notes could be presented as a town walking tour with information on places of interest and importance – the forum, shops, baths, amphitheatre, town walls and so on.

The Anglo-Saxons (page 115)

Objective: To learn that the Anglo-Saxons invaded Britain and that invasion was followed by settlement.

What to do: Talk to the class about the four big questions: *Who were the Saxons? What did they do? When did they do it? Why did they do it?* Then ask the children to read through the sheet, cut out the boxes and match them up using the clues embedded in the text, and any other knowledge that they might have. The matched pictures and text could be mounted on paper, in books, or used to make a class display.

Differentiation: Provide reference books and resource material for children to use. (The photocopiable sheet could be used as a test of existing knowledge or at the end of a project on the Anglo-Saxons.) Assist less able children with the reading, perhaps by setting up mixed-ability groups.

Extension: You could follow up any of the questions raised in more detail. Children might report their investigations to the class in the form of a short talk. Divide the children into four or more groups to answer a question each. For example, one group might make a big illustrated timeline showing the sequence of invasions, and a similar approach can be used with the other three issues.

Grave treasure (page 116)

Objectives: To understand that archaeologists can learn a great deal from discoveries such as Sutton Hoo; to make inferences from evidence.

What to do: This activity needs to be set in the context of teaching about archaeology and the amazing discoveries at Sutton Hoo. In 1939, excavations of the largest of a group of low circular mounds on a plateau overlooking the estuary of the river Debden in Suffolk revealed a magnificent Saxon ship-burial and fabulous finds of great beauty and value. There was a large collection of silver and gold clasps and buckles, a helmet with a face mask, a large shield and a superb sword. The find is thought to be the grave of Raedwald, King of the East Angles, who died around AD625. The finds had to be kept hidden in the London Underground during World War II, but are now held in the visitor centre at Sutton Hoo. Examine the intricate and beautiful design of the piece on the sheet, then let the children attempt to complete the clasp. Provide small mirrors to enable them to check the symmetrical pattern. Then discuss the object. What would a shoulder clasp have held?

Differentiation: Limit children who find this particularly challenging to completing a small section only. They could trace over the design with chalk and then fold the paper to make a 'reflection' print.

Extension: Investigate the site of Sutton Hoo. *Where was it? When were these discoveries made? What else was discovered there?* Ask children to produce a newspaper report of the day it was found, with dramatic headlines and pictures.

It's a riddle (page 117)

Objective: To find out about the way of life of the Anglo-Saxons.

What to do: Ask the children if they know any riddles, then introduce them to the word puzzles on the sheet. The originals are recorded in a large handwritten manuscript given as a gift to Exeter cathedral 1000 years ago. It was written between 950 and AD1000. Extracts are available in modern translations. See, for example, *Anglo-Saxon Poetry*, edited by SAJ Bradley (Everyman Classics). Can the children work out the answers? The illustrations provide the answers if used in conjunction with the text. Ask the children to write down the answers or cut out the pictures and text and stick them in a book.

Differentiation: Less able children should treat this as a matching activity. Can they match pictures to text? There is some difficult vocabulary, so give help with reading where required. More able children should be challenged to explain their answers, orally or in writing. What clues helped them to unravel the puzzle?

Extension: Ask children to write and illustrate a modern riddle of their own. Display them as puzzles for the rest of the class to solve. You could also read the story of Beowulf and challenge children to find out about Beowulf for homework.

Saxon dress (page 118)

Objective: To learn about the way of life of the Anglo-Saxons: how they dressed.

What to do: Explain that we can know something of what people wore in the past through archaeological finds and from information about natural dyes and so on. Chemical tests enable us to learn about the colours of Saxon cloth fragments that have been found. The leaves of the woad plant provided bright blue; the weld plant, boiled, gave bright yellow; red came from madder. By mixing these, other colours could be made. Make sure children understand that not everyone dressed in exactly the same way and that there were fashion changes even in Saxon times (shirts got longer, for example). Draw parallels with today. Ask the children to draw a connecting line from each description to the garment to which it refers. Encourage them to find the easy ones first, as they can then get the more difficult ones by a process of elimination.

Differentiation: There are some Saxon words that the children will enjoy learning, but you will need to read and explain these as they are new and strange. Let less able children work in supportive groups.

Extension: Challenge children to find out why we know very little about Saxon dress. (Cloth rots quickly and little has been preserved.) Can they find out what a Saxon warrior looked like?

A Viking longboat (page 119)

Objective: To learn about Viking longboats.

What to do: It might be worth making an OHT of the sheet so that you can have a class lesson about longboats (or longships – both terms are used). Longboats varied in size according to the task for which they were designed. One ship from the Skuldelev excavation has a draught of only one metre, but is wide with a strengthened bottom and was probably used for cargo and trade. The prow of the Gokstad ship was carved with a dragon's head, and below the water line, the overlapping planks (strakes) were only 2.5cm thick, which made the ship light and flexible in heavy seas. Make sure the children recognise that one of the drawings is a detail from the main picture drawn from a different angle.

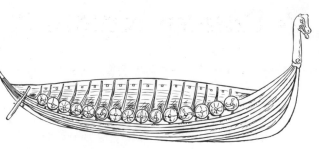

Differentiation: Less able children should tackle this sheet in a supportive group.

Extension: Lots of fun can be had with a project on the Vikings. The children could, for example: complete the picture of the ship on the sheet – add sails, colour the shields, add warriors; make models of a Viking longboat; prepare an inventory for a raid on Britain in a longboat; tell the story of a journey across the North Sea and so on.

Raiders from across the sea

(page 120)

Objective: To understand where the Vikings originated and that they explored many parts of the world.

What to do: It may be advisable to ask the children to put a coloured line around all the coastlines on the map to distinguish the land from the sea. This then becomes a straightforward interrogation of the map in order to answer the questions. The map shows northern Europe broadly as it was 1000 years ago. Children will need a reasonable atlas to answer all of the questions.

Differentiation: Give additional support by spending time exploring an atlas with the children. Can they find Britain? Can they find America? Show them how to relate the map on the sheet to the map in their atlases. You may also need to help with the text, especially the names of the countries.

Extension: Just colouring and embellishing the map is useful in this case as it will familiarise children with the places and shapes of countries. Give children a blank outline map of the world and ask them to mark places that we know the Vikings visited. Let the children investigate a modern map of Europe and compare it with the map on the sheet.

Where Vikings settled (page 121)

Objective: To investigate where the Vikings settled in Britain.

What to do: Introduce children to the notion of place names having shared endings (such as Portsmouth, Dartmouth, Lossiemouth) and that these endings have common meanings. Although children may know some places to add to the lists, this activity will really require careful examination of a fairly high detail map of Britain. A road atlas is ideal.

Differentiation: Some children may need a little help with finding their way around a road atlas and there is no substitute for adult help here.

Extension: Children will enjoy the challenge of marking

'Viking' places with a red spot on an outline map of Britain. Introduce other Viking endings for this purpose, such as *-beck* (brook), *-fell* (mountain), *-forth* (fjord), *-gill* (glen), *-with* (wood), *-scale* (house). This will reveal the pattern of 'Danelaw' settlement.

A kenning shield (page 122)

Objective: To understand something about the Viking way of life.

What to do: Explain carefully what a kenning is. This is probably best done by giving examples, such as *iron horse* for *train*. Read the examples on the sheet and consider why a fire is called a *house stealer*. Then ask the children to make up their own kennings to describe the Viking objects on the shield. They could try a couple out on rough paper before transferring the finished kenning to the shield. You might have a competition to write the best kenning.

Differentiation: Imagination and invention is needed to succeed at this task. Where children are struggling, tackle the problem in a small group, as they can help to spark each other off.

Extension: Examine the objects more carefully as evidence. What can be inferred about the Viking way of life and the technical skills that they possessed? (They used readily available natural materials, animal bone and so on; wood was used extensively; they wore jewellery; smiths made all sorts of iron objects; they had the skills to fix a comb with rivets and so on.) Find time to look at the artefacts found at Jorvik (York). If you are within striking distance, a visit is a great asset.

A Roman legionary

Read the passage and choose words to use in the labels.

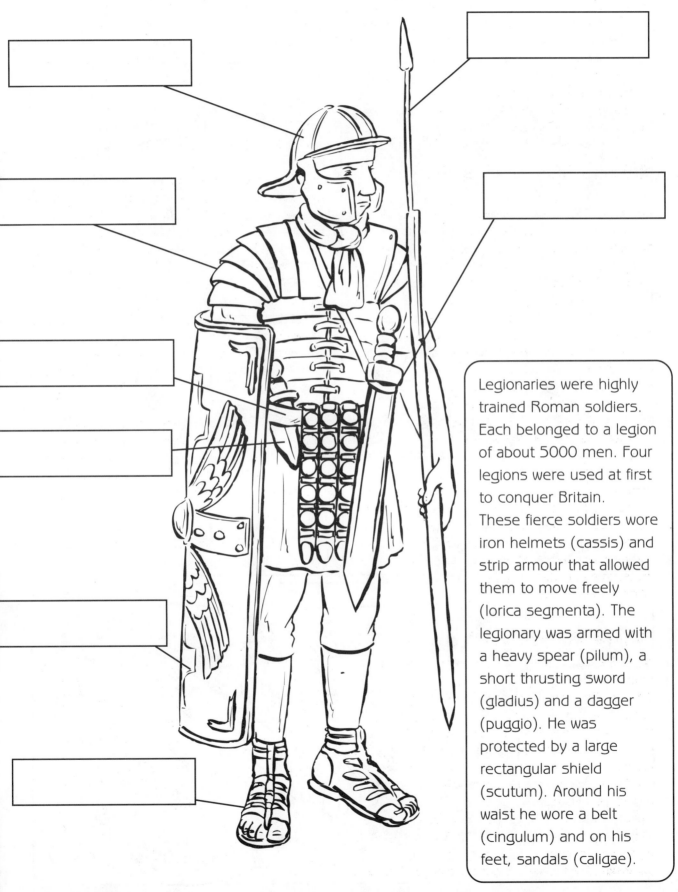

Legionaries were highly trained Roman soldiers. Each belonged to a legion of about 5000 men. Four legions were used at first to conquer Britain. These fierce soldiers wore iron helmets (cassis) and strip armour that allowed them to move freely (lorica segmenta). The legionary was armed with a heavy spear (pilum), a short thrusting sword (gladius) and a dagger (puggio). He was protected by a large rectangular shield (scutum). Around his waist he wore a belt (cingulum) and on his feet, sandals (caligae).

Roman buildings in Britain

After the Romans invaded Britain, they built **forts** for their soldiers and a great **wall** to protect their northern frontier. They also built splendid farms and country houses (**villas**) and **towns** with markets, temples, **theatres**, baths and public buildings. What do these pictures show?

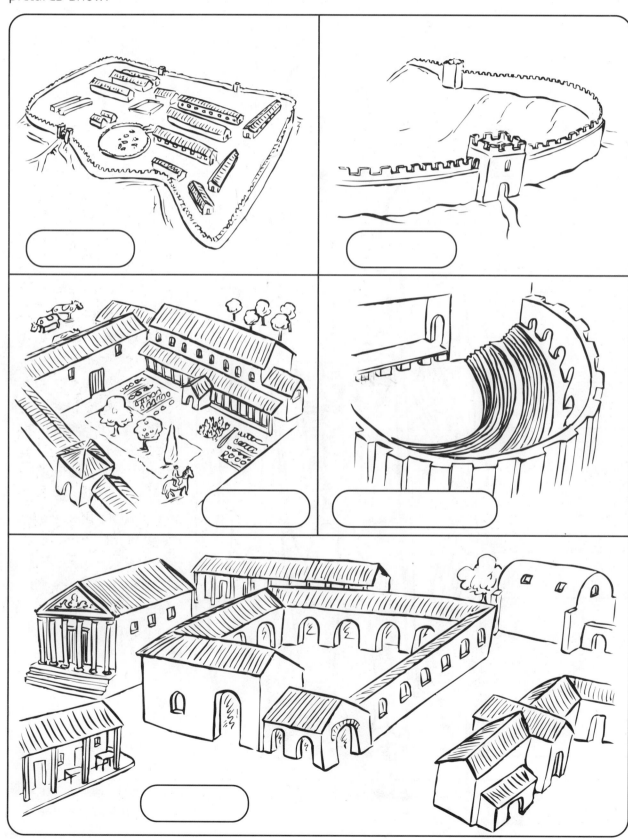

Roman mosaics

Mosaic floors were laid in public buildings and in the homes of wealthy people. The craftsman (mosaicist) made the floor pattern with cubes of coloured stone and tile called **tesserae**. This design is a **guilloche** chain.

Colour in the mosaic after looking carefully at evidence and patterns in Roman mosaics.

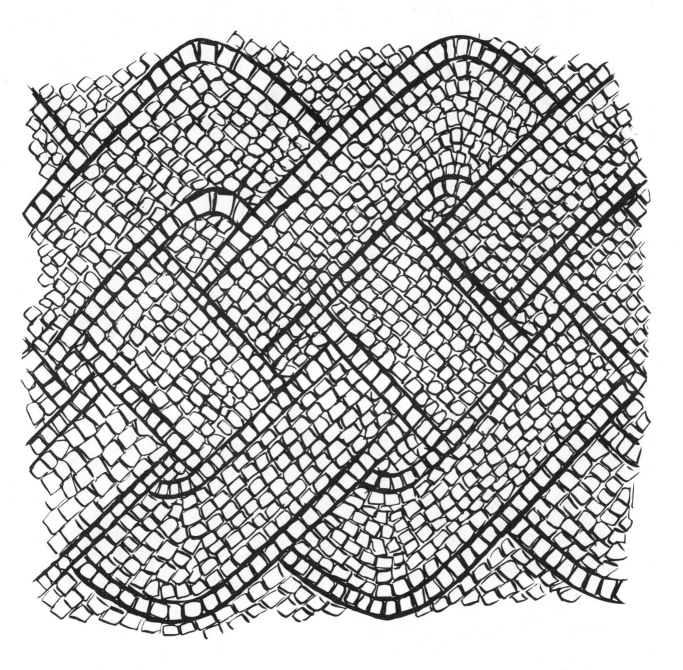

Roman mosaics are still being discovered. They have been buried under the soil for over 1000 years.

Public baths

Everyone enjoyed a trip to the public baths. Rome had about 1000 at one time! The baths started out as places to wash, but eventually became more like modern health clubs, with snack bars and sports facilities, and these were quite common across the Roman Empire.

This letter was written nearly 2000 years ago.

I live right over a public bath. Imagine the voices that irritate my ears. I can hear the groans of the musclemen as they swing their lead weights. They gasp and hiss. I also have to put up with the noisy slapping and pummelling of someone having a massage. Sometimes I will hear a ball-player loudly shouting out the score, or an angry drunk bellowing. Another man keeps singing in his bath and there are always people diving into the water with a splash. The hair plucker never stops shrieking, but his customers shriek even louder when he plucks their armpits. I am worn out by listening to people selling drinks, sausages and pastries. I am definitely finished.

Imagine you were selling this flat. Write the estate agent's details.

The Anglo-Saxons

Cut out the pictures and text, then match them up.

A Saxon village

Invasions

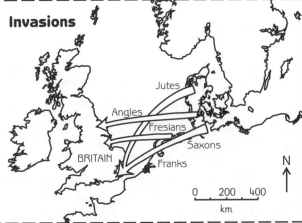

Timeline

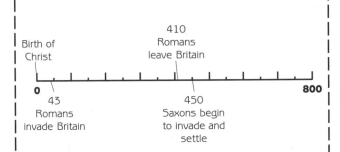

Saxon warriors

When did they invade?

The Anglo-Saxons tried to attack Britain before the Romans had left. Once the Romans had gone, they began to invade and settle.

What did they do?

Over a period of many years, the Anglo-Saxons came to Britain. They fought with the people living here and gradually conquered. They settled down to live in peace.

Who were they?

These invaders came mostly from where Denmark and Germany now are. They were called 'Saxons' by the Celts, but were Fresians, Franks, Jutes, Angles and Saxons.

Why did they invade and settle in Britain?

Some Saxons were invited here as soldiers, but generally they came to find new land to farm.

Grave treasure

A grave of a Saxon king was found at Sutton Hoo in Suffolk. It contained wonderful treasures. The Saxons who made clasps like this were very skilled craftsmen. They loved making symmetrical patterns. Can you complete this one? It is based on a shoulder clasp of gold and enamel found at Sutton Hoo.

It's a riddle

The Saxons were great storytellers and they also loved riddles. Try to solve these.

A man clad me in protective boards, covered me with hide and decked me with gold. The smith decorated me. I am an advantage to all people. What am I?

I am wounded by weapon of iron, scarred by sword, weary from action, exhausted from the edges of the blade. Often I see battle and fight the foe.

My father and mother abandoned me. Then a kindly wife covered me with clothes, kept me and cherished me as her own child.

An amazing thing happened at sea. The water turned to bone!

Saxon dress

There were changes in dress in Saxon times, just as there are fashion changes today. We have evidence that some Saxon men and women would have looked something like this. Show what these labels refer to. Then colour the clothes. Saxons had yellow, red, blue and green and mixed them to make other colours like purple.

haet – a kind of round cap worn by men

braccas – close-fitting trousers

mentel – outer cloak

belt fastened by a buckle

knife fastened to the belt

leather shoes

amber or glass beads

wrist clasp to fasten cuffs

cyrtel – a gown fastened by shoulder brooches

A Viking longboat

Number the labels according to the diagram.

A longboat had pairs of holes for **oars**.

Shields were hung on the **gunwhale**.

The side planks – **strakes** – overlapped.

Each oarsman sat in a **room**.

The vessel was built on a heavy oak **keel**.

Longboats could be steered using a **steerboard** on the right-hand side at the stern.

The strakes were fixed using **iron nails**. Joins were filled with tar to keep out the water.

Gokstad longboat

A longboat found in Gokstad, Norway was 23 metres long. It had been buried with a man, along with 6 dogs, 12 horses and a peacock.

Raiders from across the sea

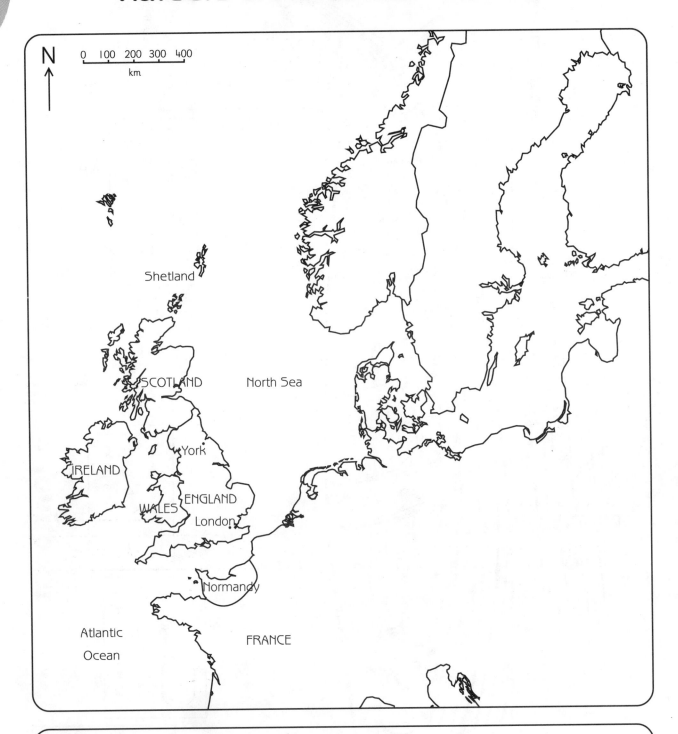

- The Vikings came from Scandinavia. Colour in and label the Scandinavian countries shown here.

- What sea did the Vikings cross to invade Britain? _____

- Draw arrows on the map to show the direction they travelled.

- On an atlas or globe, find these places that the Vikings also settled in: France, Finland, Iceland, Greenland, Russia, Newfoundland, Istanbul.

Where Vikings settled

Some Viking names for the places where they settled are still used today. Look at these Viking word-endings. Do you know any places to include in these lists? Use a map to find some more.

-by (farm or village)

Derby

-thorpe (small village)

Scunthorpe

-thwaite (clearing or paddock)

Braithwaite

-toft (piece of ground, farm)

Lowestoft

A kenning shield

The Vikings liked to tell stories and play with words. They were very fond of kennings, for example:

> ground ship   (**horse**)
> house stealer   (**fire**)

Look at these Viking objects and make up kennings for them. Write them in the rim of the shield.

GEOGRAPHY

Children's progressive geographical development in the areas defined by the National Curriculum ('geographical enquiry and skills' and 'knowledge and understanding of places, patterns and processes, and environmental change and sustainable development') takes place through the topics set down in the Breadth of Study section of the curriculum. The QCA Scheme of Work suggests two units of study to cover these topics, with an estimated time allocation of between 20 and 31 hours. In addition to this, it proposes two overarching units for the entire key stage ('What's in the news?' and 'Connecting ourselves to the world') that might be continually dipped into throughout Key Stage 2.

Although 'weather' as a discrete theme is no longer a statutory requirement of the curriculum, it inevitably comes into studies of locations and environments and, as QCA show in its matrix of curriculum coverage (Revised Appendix 4 in *Geography Teacher's Guide Update 2000*), learning about it does meet many programme of study requirements.

Fieldwork and the study of localities, both local and around the world, form an essential part of Year 3 geography, and we have tried to produce activities of a generic nature that can help to underpin studies of named localities.

Land use (page 125)

Objective: To investigate places: land use in settlements.

What to do: Study the illustration on the sheet with the children. *What sort of place is it? How can we tell? What happens here?* Tell the children to examine the map, looking for different types of land use. Discuss these categories and list the terms on a board or flip chart (roads/transport, services, houses, shops, farming, factories) before asking the children to complete the sheet themselves. The children could devise a system of colour coding to show for these areas and colour the map accordingly.

Differentiation: You could easily limit or expand the categories of land use given on the worksheet (for example, add *recreation*) to make the activity easier or more difficult. You could also dispense with the requirement to fill in labels if you use a colour-coding scheme.

Extension: Use an outline map of your town, village or local area and carry out the same exercise for real. You will need to do some fieldwork with the children and/or have some good aerial photographs for use during the activity.

Job sort (page 126)

Objective: To classify types of work.

What to do: Discuss the categories of job given on the sheet. Talk about what is involved in each and make sure the children understand the different locations and contexts. Discussion is the important element of working through this activity and should emphasise that the categories and definitions of occupations are subject to personal judgement.

Differentiation: Some help may be required with reading and writing as well as sorting. You could ask children struggling with writing to simply link the words to the sets with different-coloured lines rather than writing out the whole word.

Extension: Ask children to add more jobs and places of work to the sheet. What about parents, grandparents, neighbours? Can they suggest other categories (for example, retired, unemployed, professional)? You could also help children to conduct an occupations survey. Let the class examine and talk about information given in *Yellow Pages*. Are there any new categories suggested by this directory?

Climate (page 127)

Objective: To identify hot and cold places on a map or globe.

What to do: Wherever they study, children will need to get to grips with the notion of climate, so make sure that this concept is one they are familiar with. Use a globe to help your explanations. Ask if they have been anywhere particularly hot or cold. Introduce some of the other less-familiar vocabulary used, such as *mild* and *Equator*. Insist on light colouring on the sheet to avoid obscuring the details.

Differentiation: All the children should have access

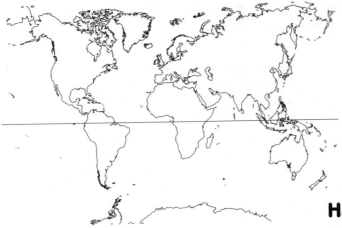

© PHOTODISC

Differentiation: Reduce the number of tasks for less able children. You might want to focus on only one main task, such as planning the route. Children could also work in pairs.

Extension: Make a holiday postcard display. Ask children to bring in a postcard from home and describe to the class what the place is like. Sort the postcards into categories according to type of holiday, climate, location and so on.

to suitable reference books. Make a display showing hot and cold lands. Play games with a globe to familiarise children with places on it (an inflatable globe that can be tossed around the classroom is useful – one child throws to another with the instruction *Find a cold place* and so on).

Extension: Introduce the idea of 'zones'. Is Britain in a hot, cold or mild zone? Challenge children to find out which climatic zone certain places are in. This could be a homework task.

Happy holidays (1) (page 128)

Objective: To understand how climate affects human activity.

What to do: Examine the postcard on the sheet with the class (and show similar examples if you have them). Ask: *Where is it? What is it like there? What sort of activities could you do on holiday in this place? How would you get there?* Use some of the places on postcards you have collected to let the children practise using the contents and index in an atlas. Talk about why people go on holiday, relating this to weather patterns and climate. You will need simple world maps for the children to mark on and, ideally, large blank picture postcards for them to write on for the last part of the activity.

Happy holidays (2) (page 129)

Objective: To understand how climate affects human activity.

What to do: This activity is in the same vein as 'Happy holidays (1)', above, but for a cold place with different activities.

Differentiation/extension: These will be the same as 'Happy holidays (1)'.

Banff holidays

© PHOTODISC

Where did it happen? (page 130)

Objective: To investigate places using secondary sources.

What to do: This sheet is a good introduction to investigating places and stories in newspapers and on television. Explain to the children that they should read the headlines and extracts and note down where each event is taking place. Ask them to find the places in a map or atlas of the UK.

Differentiation: Put less competent children in a group and have an adult or older child to act as reader or to help with the atlas work.

Extension: Bring in a local newspaper and ask children to locate the stories on a local outline map (estate agents are often a good source of these). Display the cuttings of selected news items on a class news board. This idea can be extended to use a world map to cover international news.

It's nice in Nice

© PHOTODISC

What is the land used for? Complete the labels.

Land use

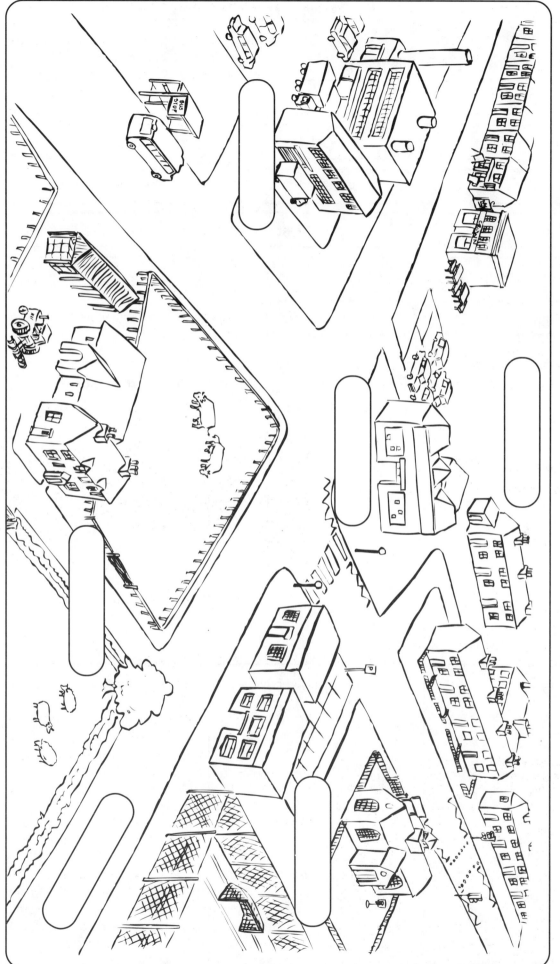

Job sort

Put these jobs into the groups below.

secretary	doctor	car production worker
bank manager	teacher	garage mechanic
taxi driver	salesperson	checkout operator
bank clerk	receptionist	nurse
shelf stacker	refuse collector	farmer
brick layer	bus driver	

shop	**services**	**transport**
factory	**office**	**other**

Climate

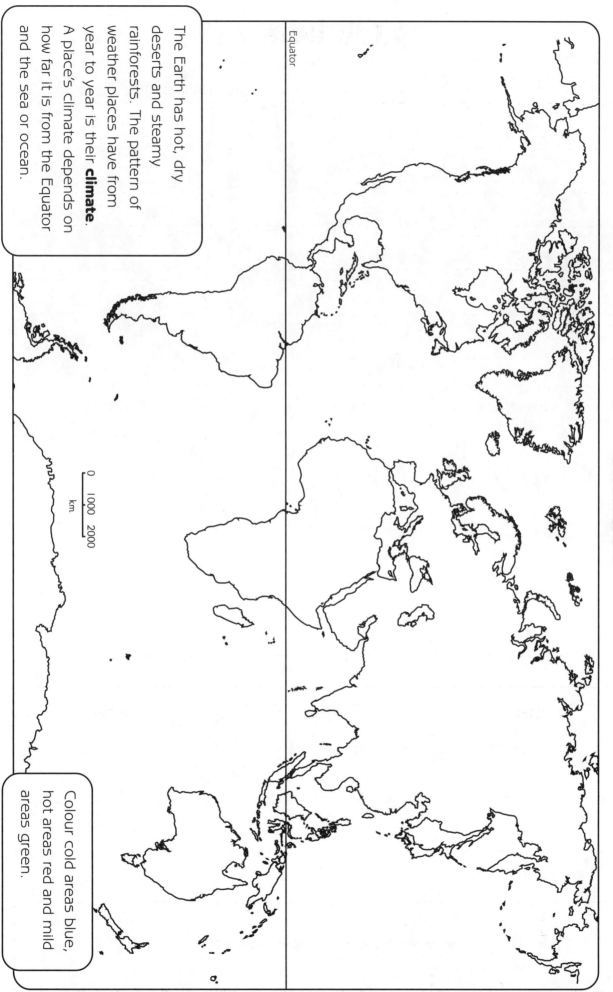

The Earth has hot, dry deserts and steamy rainforests. The pattern of weather places have from year to year is their **climate**. A place's climate depends on how far it is from the Equator and the sea or ocean.

Equator

Colour cold areas blue, hot areas red and mild areas green.

0   1000   2000
km

Happy holidays (1)

It's nice in Nice

© PHOTODISC

● Find this place in your atlas. What country is it in? _____

● What transport would you use to get here? _____

_____

● Plan your route on a map of the world.

● Make a list of what you would pack for a holiday here. _____

_____

_____

● Write a postcard to a friend saying what you have been doing at this holiday
destination and what the weather is like.

Happy holidays (2)

Banff holidays

© PHOTODISC

● Find this place in your atlas. What country is it in? _____

● What transport would you use to get here? _____

_____

● Plan your route on a map of the world.

● Make a list of what you would pack for a holiday here. _____

_____

_____

● Write a postcard to a friend saying what you have been doing at this holiday destination and what the weather is like.

Where did it happen?

1. Asylum seeker sought

Police were at a loss last night as whereabouts of 20 asylum seekers made an escape from a centre to Dover. How the escape given that it was Friday but new

2. Top DJ stops spinning

but the time has come to stop for 25 years. So tomorrow will turn up at the in central London

3. Property of the week

Nettlefield Farm near Doncaster is very reasonable price of £1m

4. Cliffhanger in Dorset

After the heavy rains of winter declared unsafe. What will happen to properties in the area east of the Lyme Regis itself should unnecessary panic crabs and by boat but council efforts

5. Pay as you worship?

It is becoming the fashion for the cathedrals of the land to charge fees for everyone who wants to go Gloucester Cathedral has so far the temptation to change

● List the places in the news.

1._____   4._____

2._____   5._____

3._____

● Find them on a map.

DESIGN AND TECHNOLOGY

More than anything, design and technology in the National Curriculum is concerned with developing ideas – planning, making products, and evaluating them. This can be done by (1) investigating familiar products, (2) practical tasks (for developing skills and techniques) and (3) designing and making products. Practical experience is the key to all learning in this subject. This is time consuming and it is worth noting that the QCA Scheme of Work for Year 3 could take up between 31 and 39 hours. The design-and-make element of the scheme has been included in some of these worksheets, which means that using them generally involves the need for materials and equipment, close supervision and appropriate health and safety precautions. If sandwiches are made, for example, then hygiene is particularly important (and a part of the teaching programme). The sheets cannot cover everything but they do provide support for the basic curriculum elements for design and technology.

Packaging for a purpose (page 133)

Objective: To investigate how materials have been used to make packaging fit for purpose, and to consider stiffness and stability in design.

What to do: Accompany the activity on this sheet with hands-on examination of a real cereal packet. Although children will have experienced this and, with the aid of the illustration could probably manage to answer most of the questions without hands-on work, there is no substitute for the real thing if the activity is to be done properly. Before the children complete the sheet, make sure that they do not attack the assignment in a superficial way. For example, the answer to the second question is not simply *cereal*, as there is usually an inner bag too (although this is part of the packaging). The children should consider: *What is the function of the box? What is it made of? Why? Does it work?* Work on this sheet is an example of 'interrogating' evidence. The answers come from the examination of the object. Discuss the children's answers as a whole class. Use vocabulary such as *packaging, edge, face, adhesive, join* and *capacity*.

Differentiation: Provide some (empty) packets for the children to pull apart and examine properly. Adult supervision may be needed to focus some children's

attention on the specific tasks. Answers could be written by a group scribe, perhaps an adult.

Extension: Challenge children to look at the last question in more detail. You could scan the design into a computer for children to manipulate. Ask them to make their own cereal-box artwork. *What information must it contain? What is its purpose?* This could be a homework task, or an ICT activity, if you have suitable software.

Nets (1) (page 134)

Objectives: To understand that a 3-D shape can be constructed from a net and that the 3-D shape depends upon the shape of the net; to develop skills in cutting, scoring and assembling.

What to do: Introduce nets to the children and ask them to think about the shape that the net on the sheet would make. Tell them to cut out the outline as instructed (avoiding the fold lines) and stick it firmly onto thin card. When dry, the dotted lines can be scored. Show children how to do this carefully. Demonstrate how to do the task safely and warn the children of the possible dangers. Consider how the cube can be permanently joined. Allow them to use adhesive tape at this stage. The faces of the cube can be coloured (before joining) to make pretty designs.

Differentiation: Practice at scoring and folding may be required. Children could practise on scrap card.

Extension: Some children may enjoy the challenge of trying to find a way of drawing the net so that adhesive tape will not be needed to keep it together. (The most efficient design is to use flaps on every other external edge.)

Nets (2) (page 135)

Objective: To explore how nets are made using flat shapes.

What to do: Remind the children of the net of a cube that they have already handled and ask them to think about the 'reverse'. Let the children try out ideas for nets of the objects on the sheet. Explain that their drawings are not meant to be plans that will be cut out and assembled. They may come up with several attempts. After they have selected their design, it should be discussed (perhaps by the whole class). *Can anyone see why it might not work?* The object is not necessarily to get the 'right' answer, but to begin to think about the transformation from two to three dimensions. The nets are basically the same as that for a cube – only the flat shapes are different (rectangles and triangles instead of squares).

Differentiation: There is no substitute for examining and disassembling the real thing, so provide packages for children to handle and take apart.

Extension: Let children have a go at assembling one of their nets. Provide card or plastic shapes for them to draw around (of appropriate shapes and dimensions). The level of geometrical drawing skill required to do it any other way is likely to be too much at this age.

Design and make (page 136)

Objective: To create a package for a given purpose and to consider the need to make designs stable.

What to do: Help the children to read and understand the instructions and checklist on the sheet. You will need to have discussed the many purposes of packaging. The children can complete the first part of the activity on the sheet, but they will need materials – glue, scissors and so on to make their design. Ask them to draw detailed designs, test the product, and discuss improvements that may have been noted in the checklist. Encourage them to try the design (that is, make a mock-up) in paper first before using card or other more expensive materials. Let them make some 'play' sweets to go into the package.

Differentiation: Give children time to experiment to complete this activity. Adult support should be on hand, but don't interfere too readily. Children must have time and space to learn by trial and success.

Extension: Discuss how far the design and the product measures up to the criteria that the children set down at the top of the sheet. *Does it do what it was intended to do? Where does it leave room for improvement? What could be done to make it better?*

Sandwich selection (page 137)

Objective: To identify that different sandwiches are created for different needs, occasions and purposes.

What to do: The children may need access to reference material to get to know the sandwiches listed on the sheet. They could print off pictures from computer sources instead of using drawings. The challenge at the bottom of the sheet demands considerable attention. The children could answer it simply, but the design-and-make aspect of this challenge should be considered, so encourage them to create and name their own sandwich.

Differentiation: Some children may need help in using reference material. They should work in pairs and an adult should be available to help if needed.

Extension: Ask children to describe an occasion for which each of the listed sandwiches might make a suitable snack, such as picnics, midday break, cycling excursion, lunch during a shopping trip, school lunch. You could help children design and make a sandwich for Sara. This needs planning and careful teaching. (See the QCA unit 'Sandwich snacks' for ideas.)

Pneumatic gnome (page 138)

Objective: To develop an understanding of a simple pneumatic system and to construct one that works.

What to do: The children undertake a design-and-make assignment for this activity, so you will need to provide the equipment illustrated (squeezable plastic bottle, suitable diameter plastic tubing, balloon, small plastic flowerpot). You should also have card, scissors and glue to hand for the design and fixing of the gnome. Yoghurt cartons make a suitable support on which to 'sit' the gnome inside the pot. Ideally, you should try this out yourself to make sure that the materials are of compatible sizes. Although you might demonstrate the part inflation of the balloon, the children must solve the problems of designing and making for themselves. You should pose questions such as: *What will the gnome be made of? How will he sit in the pot without falling over? How will the pneumatic system help to solve the problem of raising the gnome?* All these issues should be considered before hacking and gluing begins.

Differentiation: Differentiate by the allocation of time. Allow plenty of time for less able children to complete this activity. They could also work in pairs.

Extension: Can children think up another use for this sort of system? (It could open the lid of a box, raise a clown's hat, push Santa back up the chimney…) You could try using plastic syringes for accurate control of the air input to the system.

Packaging for a purpose

- Think about a cereal packet.

- What does it protect?

- What does it contain?

- What material is it made from?

- How is it stiffened?

- What information does it show?

Nets (1)

● This is the net of a three-dimensional (3-D) shape. If you cut it out and fold it, what 3-D shape will be made?

● Stick the net onto card. Score the dotted lines. Cut and fold to make the shape.

● Can you draw a different net for the same 3-D shape?

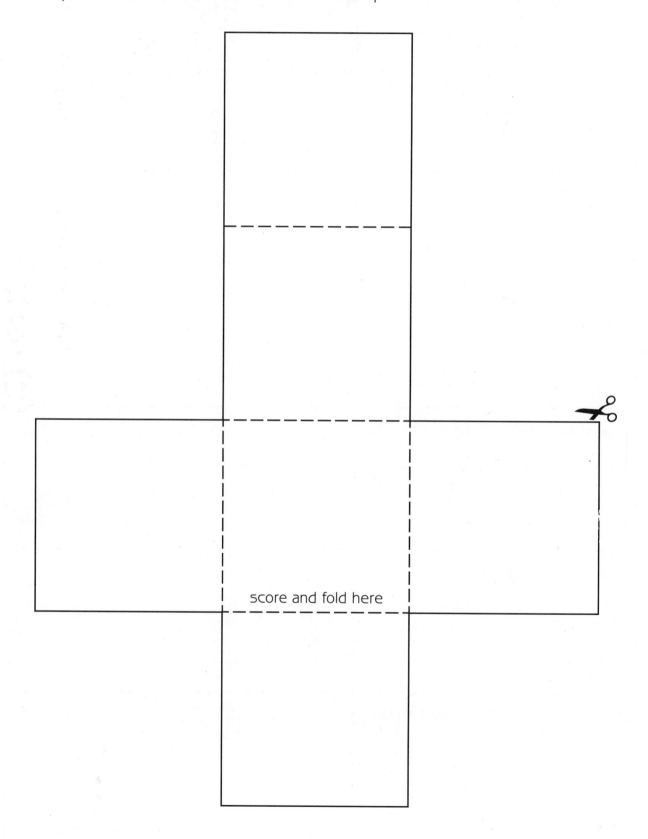

score and fold here

Nets (2)

What might the nets of these packages look like? Sketch your ideas.

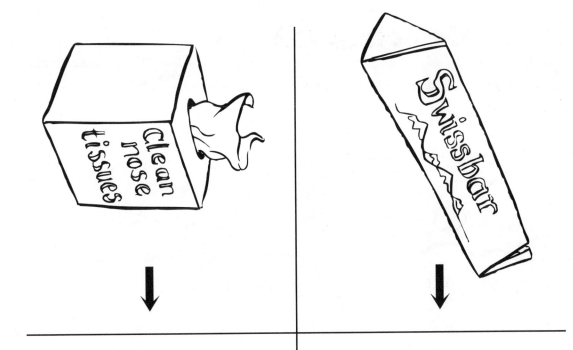

Design and make

A sweet factory needs a package for its new chocolates. It is your job to design and make it.

Think!

Design

● What does the package need to do?

_____

_____

_____

_____

● Draw your idea.

● Make it.

Checklist

What is it made from?	
Is it stiff enough?	
Does it need strengthening?	
How could it be improved?	
Does it do everything you wanted it to?	

Sandwich selection

● Find out about these different sandwiches.

Name	Description	Illustration
open sandwich		
double-decker sandwich		
toasted sandwich		
filled pitta		
club sandwich		

● What sandwich would you make for Sara to eat on a cold winter's day? What ingredients would you use?

Pneumatic gnome

● Try this!

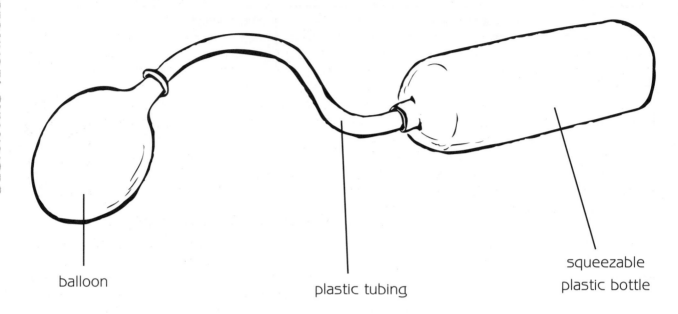

balloon

plastic tubing

squeezable
plastic bottle

● Squeeze the bottle. What happens? _____

● Use what you have discovered to make a gnome pop out of a flowerpot.

ICT

At the heart of ICT teaching lies the computer. It is not a machine to be used as an add-on, an afterthought, or optional convenience gadget. In the early days of its introduction into schools, it wasn't uncommon to find children instructed to copy handwritten text into the computer in the belief that this was word-processing. It wasn't – it was copy typing. We have tried to avoid compounding similar preconceptions in constructing these worksheets and in consequence have limited ourselves in what we should tackle. When the National Curriculum and the QCA Scheme of Work detail combining text and graphics, manipulating sound, using databases, exploring simulations and e-mail, it is intended that children are involved in hands-on computer work, not pencil and paper activities.

However, all of the sheets offered here give the children a context from which to undertake particular tasks on the computer, and although the work on the sheet usually begins without the necessity of a keyboard or mouse, it doesn't finish in that way. The activities support some of the five units included in the QCA scheme, each requiring hardware, software and an unspecified amount of time.

blocky
thin
office

skeleton
rounded
old
squashed

fancy
falling

happy

Fitting fonts (page 141)

Objective: To learn how to alter font size, type and colour for emphasis and effect.

What to do: Introduce the children to the terms *font* and *graphics*. Examine various examples of shapes, sizes and styles of printed text from a number of different sources. Make sure that the children understand the instructions on the sheet and point out that the words beneath the chart are printed using a variety of sizes, fonts and graphic effects and are numbered. The children should use their judgement to match the meaning of each word to a style that best suits it. In some cases, this might appear fairly straightforward, for example a 'dropping' font effect for the word *falling*, but to some extent it must be a matter of judgement and taste, so there are no definitive answers. Having completed the first part of the sheet, ask the children to use the computer to explore the possibilities of font choice and size, and here colour can be introduced.

Differentiation: The only support likely to be required is help with reading difficult words, but you may need to instruct and support some children in the use of the computer for this specific task, depending on the children's previous experience.

Extension: Give children practice in editing text by highlighting and overtyping. They should also be able to save amended text.

Business card mix-up (page 142)

Objective: To combine graphics and text to communicate information.

What to do: If you can get hold of some, show the children a few genuine business cards. Alternatively, you could use advertisements in *Yellow Pages* as a similar type of example. Discuss how business cards can communicate the information that they need to in a small space and using few words. Let the children have fun spotting the errors in the cards on the sheet and writing comments below each card. Finally, ask them to design a business card (or small *Yellow Pages* advertisement) for another local service. You will need to demonstrate or recap with the children how to locate, retrieve and add graphics to text. They may also need to be shown how to resize text and graphics to make them fit together.

Differentiation: This is likely to be mainly a matter of allowing the slower computer users more time to practise techniques and to work their way through the activity.

Extension: Discuss where pictures and decorations can come from for this sort of project. Teach children how to capture and use images from a scanner or digital camera.

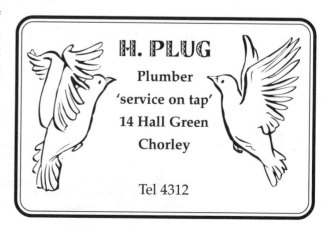

H. PLUG

Plumber
'service on tap'
14 Hall Green
Chorley

Tel 4312

Book cover (page 143)

Objective: To combine graphics and text to communicate information.

What to do: This is a more sophisticated and demanding task, but in essence builds on similar skills to those used in the previous activity. Explain to the children that they need to do a 'cut and paste' job on the mock book cover provided. Let them cut out the parts, colour the sections and paste up the arrangement as they think best suits the function of a book cover. The end product may be enhanced further by sticking the parts onto coloured backing paper. As an extension to combining graphics and text when the children design book covers, teach them (or give them further practice in) how to use new sources for pictures, such as a scanner, CD-ROM or digital camera. In helping to complete the last part of the sheet, ask the children to bring in their favourite books. Discuss the covers and ask the children to look at how they could improve the designs.

Differentiation: Limit the picture sources to those from clip art or a CD-ROM to remove a layer of difficulty for less computer-literate children.

Extension: Set similar design activities for further practice. For example, let children design an advertisement for their favourite film or television programme. Where home computers are universal, you might want to set this as a homework task, and the printed or saved designs could be brought or sent to school in an appropriate form.

Computer glossary (page 144)

Objective: To become more familiar with technical vocabulary.

What to do: Tell the children to read through the photocopiable sheet carefully. Make sure that they understand the term *glossary*. The correct meanings and words can be linked using a bold line or they could be cut out and rearranged. At some point, you should demonstrate all the terms in the glossary. Using all of the skills and knowledge that they have acquired so far, ask the children to design and print this glossary themselves, with the correct definitions. Remind them to include alphabetical order as part of their design criteria.

Differentiation: Help may be needed with reading the text. Show examples wherever children are not familiar with the terms.

Extension: The curriculum programme of study requires that children are introduced to e-mail so, assuming that all the other terms in the glossary on the sheet are understood, help children to use and practise e-mail by setting up a line of communication, perhaps with someone in another class or another school. For advice on how to go about this, consult your ICT co-ordinator or county advisor. Unit 3E in the QCA Scheme of Work sets out an approach you might want to follow.

Fitting fonts

● On a computer, you can choose a font that is the size, shape and colour to fit the job it has to do. These fonts have not been used in the best way. Choose the font numbers that would match the meanings of these words.

Word	Font number

1. blocky
2. thin
3. office
4. skeleton
5. rounded
6. old
7. squashed
8. fancy
9. falling
10. happy

● Use the computer to try out the words with different fonts, weights and colours.

Business card mix-up

● Examine these business cards. Look at the font, frames, size of letters and illustrations. What is wrong? Note down how you would improve them.

John Coffin & daughter
Undertakers

5 The Mount
Heckmondwike
Tel 22541

We offer a comforting service

H. PLUG
Plumber
'service on tap'
14 Hall Green
Chorley

Tel 4312

_____   _____

_____   _____

_____   _____

_____   _____

Gardener's Place

A tool for every job
Land's Edge, Weston
Tel 9391

Jane Ward

Vicar of Dudley

welcomes you to her cheerful church

Weddings – a speciality

_____   _____

_____   _____

_____   _____

_____   _____

● On the computer, design your own card for a local business.

Book cover

● Cut out the text and pictures below and arrange them to make a book cover.

by Justin Thyme

published by Adventurelogue Ltd

FLIGHT TO EGYPT

● Use a computer to design a cover for your favourite book.

Computer glossary

● Match the terms to their definitions.

font

> messages sent from one person to another using a computer and telephone line

highlight

> digital art that can be placed in documents

align left/right

> place text or pictures in the middle of a page

centre

> style of type, for example Futura, Times, Helvetica

frame

> start the beginning of each object or line of text against an unseen vertical line on the left or finishing against one on the right

graphics

> select and shade text or pictures to make them stand out

e-mail

> enclose text or pictures within lines or patterns

● Design and print this information as a glossary. Add suitable pictures.

ART AND DESIGN

'Art and design is not just a subject to learn, but an activity that you can practise: with your hands, your eyes, your whole personality.' Thus is quoted Quentin Blake in the National Curriculum – a quotation that puts the Key Stage 2 approach to art and design in a nutshell. It is not just a matter of what children have to do, but what they have to experience. One aspect of the work for Year 3 children, that also recurs in other years, is that of examining and questioning the work of creative people whether they are artists, designers, architects or sculptors. There is clearly plenty of art and design 'fieldwork' for children to do.

Given the wide-ranging aims of the curriculum, the worksheets in this section can only be a springboard for further work and experience. Children should deal with art not only on the scale of an A4 sheet. We have therefore tried to focus on what worksheets can be suited to and have had to leave the world of the tactile and sensory largely for you to deal with. The QCA scheme suggests a programme that requires between 30 and 36 hours to complete satisfactorily, although this subject is time-hungry and you may well find that you wish to allocate more. The activities here will support your teaching of art and design particularly well if you are following the approaches suggested in the QCA Scheme of Work. If you wish to study the QCA schemes in more detail, they are available at www.standards.dfee.gov.uk/schemes.

More than one (1) (page 147)

Objective: To comment on and compare approaches to group portrait work.

What to do: This sheet is a companion to 'More than one (2)'. It is intended that the children work on both sheets, but this one should be attempted first. The first aim is to get the children to make thoughtful observations about the images and relationships in double portraits. Focus their attention on the pictures to collect visual information that will lead to them developing their own ideas for a double portrait. This activity should stimulate thoughts and comments for a class discussion. It is particularly important that you talk about the relationship between the people shown: *How can you tell what their relationship is? How is this relationship shown in the picture?* (Look at pose, position, dress, expression and so on.)

© COREL

The American Farmer by Thomas Waterman Wood

It helps to consider why a picture like this was painted in the first place. Ideally, look at a number of portraits in colour and black and white before looking at this sheet (slides are useful for this purpose). Finally, let the children tackle the questions on the sheet, working with a partner. Ask them to give written answers if you feel that it is appropriate.

Differentiation: This should remain as only an oral activity for less able children, as the difficulty of writing the answers can detract from the aim of the activity. An enlarged reproduction of the portrait is useful.

Extension: Play a 'posing' game. Get the children involved in the posing of pairs of people – two friends, team members, siblings, teacher and child, mother and daughter, cook and headteacher and so on. How should they pose? Facial expression? What about the background? You could use a digital camera to record the images.

More than one (2) (page 148)

Objectives: To comment on and compare approaches to group portrait work; to make a composition showing the relationship between two people.

What to do: At first, use the same approach for this activity as for 'More than one (1)'. Then let the children try to create a double portrait for themselves. You should consider, with the children's suggestions, what medium is to be used (you might choose pencil, crayon, chalk, paint, charcoal and so on). Discuss how paint can be applied to make different effects. Light colour washes, for example, can be overpainted with darker tones. How you approach this will depend on the experiences the children have already had. For example, have they learned how to mix paint to produce different tints and tones? Also talk about how the people will be posed, for example both sitting, one or both standing?

Differentiation: All the children should be able to tackle this activity at their level. You could limit choices – of medium, colours and so on – if some children need simplification.

Extension: Ask children to bring in photographs of double portraits from home and get them to explain the relationship between the people in the portraits. Beforehand, however, see if the other children in the class can deduce what this relationship is from clues in the picture.

Patterns (1) (page 149)

Objective: To study patterns and describe different ways that they are made.

What to do: This activity is suitable as a class, group or paired activity. Ask the children to examine the examples on the sheet and then record the numbers of the patterns in the spaces where they judge that they fit best. The answers should be discussed rather than marked right or wrong, as there can be a number of interpretations and variations. Let the children know that some patterns will fit more than one question. The patterns are: 1. William Morris printed textile, 2. Indian printed textile, 3. Islamic tile, 4. Celtic knotwork, 5. Bengali Kanthas, 6. Scandinavian design, 7. Ghanaian Asafo flag.

Differentiation: Help should be given in reading and explaining the questions on the sheet, otherwise children should manage unaided.

Extension: Give children tactile as well as visual experience of patterns. Let them handle a variety of different materials and examine how the patterns are put together. Look at prints, woodcuts, tiles, fabrics and so on. For homework, you could ask children to find an example of a particular type of pattern – one based on natural objects, geometrical shapes, overlapping shapes and so on – and to consider where we use patterned designs in everyday life, such as in wallpaper, tiles and clothing.

Patterns (2) (page 150)

Objective: To explore ways of making and creating their own patterns.

What to do: Before working on the sheet, introduce the vocabulary used and create a wall display of key words and examples: *geometric shapes, symmetry, reflection, rotation, transform, translation, repeat pattern* and so on. The children will need scissors and glue for this activity. They will also need lots of repeats of their pattern. Ask the children to draw or find their own. You might want to use coloured paper, but avoid adhesive coloured paper as this will not allow the children to experiment with reflections and so on.

Differentiation: As making the pattern is the important part of the exercise, you could simplify it without undue interference to the aim by supplying ready-cut repeated shapes.

Extension: Help children to experiment with other techniques of making patterns, such as stencilling, block printing, potato printing.

What difference does it make? (page 151)

Objective: To question and make thoughtful observations about how sculptors' work can improve the quality of an environment.

What to do: Draw the children's attention to the sculptures illustrated on the sheet. You may want to let them go straight to answering the questions in the spaces, depending on how much discussion and previous work you have done on sculpture in the environment. Where they are asked to think of words that describe the sculptures, encourage them to write, say three single adjectives, not sentences.

Differentiation: Less confident children should work in a small group on this activity to discuss ideas.

Extension: If you can, go out and look at an example of sculpture in your locality. Ask children to choose a place where a sculpture might be placed to improve the area. (This links to the next activity.)

Where should it go? (page 152)

Objective: To develop ideas for a sculpture for a chosen site.

What to do: This sheet is simply to prepare the way for a 'making' activity (see extension). Ask the children to study the sculpture and the picture and think about the quality of the areas shown. Which space is in need of improvement? Might it be improved by the sculpture? You might also want to consider where the sculpture would be looked at most frequently and valued most. You could discuss these points as a whole class or set the activity as a group assignment. Ask the children to place the sculpture in the illustration using an arrow or by cutting it out and sticking it into position.

Differentiation: Some children may benefit from working in pairs.

Extension: Organise the children into small groups and ask each group to produce a 'sculpture'. There are many ways of doing this: using boxes, recycled materials, making a wire armature, using Modroc, papier mâché, paper strips and so on. You need to know your children and your materials. Refer to books of teaching techniques for details (you could try Scholastic's *Curriculum Bank: Art Key Stage Two* for some ideas). Suggestions and approaches are given in the QCA scheme Unit 3C 'Can we change places?'. You should also agree a place where this sculpture might be needed – examine the school environment, for example.

More than one (1)

● Think about this picture. Do these people know each other? How can you tell? What is the relationship between them? Why do you think the picture was painted?

● Describe:

● the people

● the pose

● the background.

© COREL

The American Farmer by Thomas Waterman Wood

◾SCHOLASTIC

More than one (2)

● Think about this picture.

Describe:

- the people
- their characters
- their relationship
- the pose
- the background.

© COREL

Mother and son, Han Chinese

● Try for yourself. Draw or paint a large portrait of two people, one of whom is yourself. How will they pose? How will they be linked together?

Patterns (1)

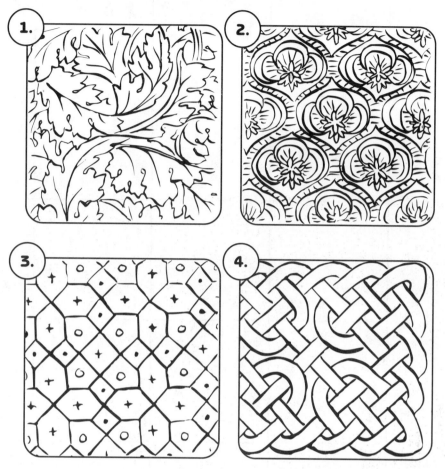

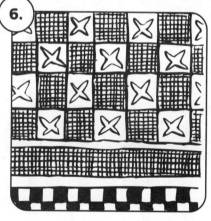

● Which patterns are made up of simple shapes? _____

● Which are based on animals, plants or objects? _____

● Which have overlapping shapes? _____

● Which have repeated shapes? _____

Patterns (2)

● Cut out lots of copies of a shape like this one, or draw your own.
● Arrange the shape in different patterns on the grid. Rotate, reflect, transform (half drop, full drop) the shape.

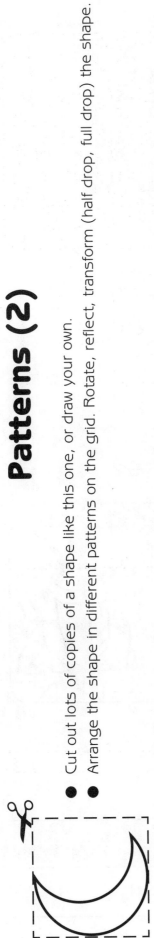

What difference does it make?

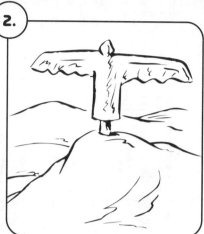

For each sculpture:

- think about why it has been put in that place
- consider if it makes a difference to the place
- think of a few words to describe it.

3.

Where should it go?

Look carefully at the place in this picture. Where would the sculpture improve it?

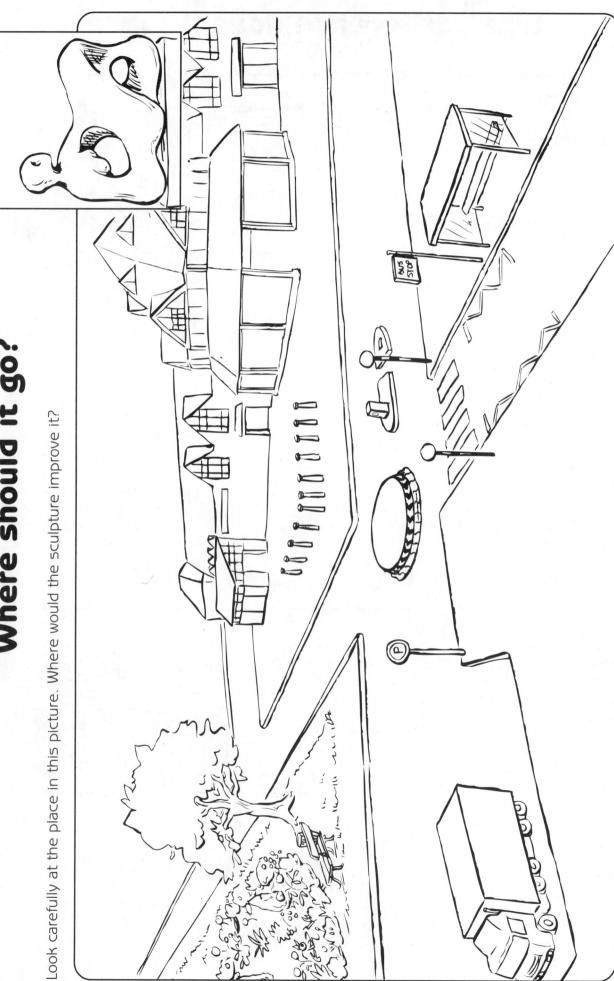

MUSIC

At the heart of the music programme for Year 3 children are musical skills that require regular practice. In particular, children are expected to develop the use of their voices, to build up a simple repertoire of songs that they can sing from memory with increasing control and accuracy, and to listen carefully. That is the background against which these supporting worksheets should be operating. However appropriate these sheets might be, they will be worth little in terms of the children's musical development if singing and music-making are not part of a regular, frequent, school experience.

The QCA Scheme of Work allocates between 9 and 18 hours to specific units of study for Year 3, plus a core unit of skills that would consume around 9 hours – giving a maximum for the year of 27 hours. Perhaps this is recognition of the difficulty many primary schools have in finding specialist expertise, but it would seem an inadequate allocation of time if performance, repetition and practice are taken into account. However, music-making does 'naturally' occur in small corners of the timetable – at the end of the day, before assembly, in assembly – and this time can accumulate considerably.

You will notice that knowledge and use of musical notation has begun to creep in at this level. You will need to know what a crotchet rest looks like and to understand the meaning of the word *ostinato*, in the same way as in ICT there is a need to know what a CD-ROM is and how to operate e-mail. Don't be shy of approaching your music co-ordinator for professional advice and support. You cannot be expected to know everything!

We must put in a small plea here that, when required, the best possible instruments and electronic methods of sound reproduction be used. Children should be given the best because, by and large, they will be used to the best in the cinema, on television and CDs, where the quality of modern sound reproduction, even on relatively cheap systems, is excellent. Help your school to aspire to high modern standards.

The frog and the snake (1) and (2) (pages 155 and 156)

Objectives: To explore descriptive sounds; to musically interpret text and illustrations; to combine narration and sound to describe particular animals.

What to do: Let the children listen to some good descriptive animal music before they attempt this activity. (Saint-Saëns' *Carnival of the Animals* is an obvious choice, but there are others, such as Leopold Mozart's *Toy Symphony*, Prokofiev's *Peter and the Wolf*, Respighi's *The Birds*, Rossini's overture *The Thieving Magpie* and *The Lark Ascending* by Vaughan Williams.) This activity is not intended to be done individually and could be undertaken by any size group of children, even a whole class. As a whole-class introduction, you could read out the story yourself, looking at the illustrations together, or help a confident child to read it with expression. Note that the story is continued onto a second sheet – 'The frog and the snake (2)', on page 156. As the narrator reads the story, ask the other children to create music to go with the words and pictures. Point out that there may be elements of the illustrations that are not mentioned in the text but are nevertheless suitable for musical interpretation, such as the clicking reeds or whispering grasses. For a whole class or large group performance, the pictures could be made into transparencies for overhead projection or scanned into a computer for a multimedia presentation. The activity can be done in a very simple way, with few children and instruments, or on a much grander scale. These are decisions that you need to make at the outset. Point out to the children that the last frame – on 'The frog and the snake (2)' – has been left blank for them to supply their own ending to the story in both words and pictures. Ask them to think about what might happen next and to consider how they could represent this in sound.

photocopiable sheet. Emphasise that an ostinato is a *repeated* pattern, so once is not enough!

Differentiation: Put less confident children in a group with an adult rhythm leader and work through the activity as a follow-my-leader game. When they have had sufficient practice, let one of the children take the lead.

Extension: The next stage is to play several ostinati at the same time to a repeated pulse. (See 'Food ostinati', below.) You could practise this with a simple song like 'London's Burning'. The three-beat pulse can be played by one group against two other groups – two beats and a rest (*Fire! Fire!* –) and two quavers and two crotchets (*Lon-don's burn-ing*).

Differentiation: Allocate tasks according to ability, although all of the children should get the opportunity to make the musical sounds. If you rotate the roles, let less able children attempt the difficult ones last, so they have a chance to see someone 'model' the task for them.

Extension: Help the children to combine the narration and music with dance and movement. In particular, talk about the various qualities of movement that the sounds will also share, for example length (short, long); level (high, low, in-between); rhythm; quality (heavy, light, smooth).

Ostinati (page 157)

Objective: To perform a repeated rhythmic pattern to a steady pulse.

What to do: Repeated rhythmic patterns are common in music, so introduce the concept to the children by letting them listen to an example (QCA documents suggest *Tubular Bells* by Mike Oldfield). The term *ostinato* should be used and become part of the children's musical vocabulary. At this age, they love getting their tongues around new words – more so than teachers perhaps! Move on to clap some rhythms as a class, based on a particular theme. For example, on a transport theme: *on – a – bus*; *go-ing – by – car* and so on. The children should then be able to use this practice to clap or play the ostinati given on the

Food ostinati (page 158)

Objective: To perform repeated rhythmic patterns to a steady pulse.

What to do: This activity follows the same pattern as 'Ostinati' above, except that the children will need to work co-operatively. Pulse is to be felt in all music, so an ostinato will fit a pattern dictated by the pulse. First, invent some food ostinati with the children (to a steady four-beat pulse) and help them get used to how this activity works. Then let the children work together in groups to perform the ostinati on the sheet for themselves.

Differentiation: Support this activity by the allocation of adult time and assistance as suggested in the notes for 'Ostinati'.

Extension: More organised performance is a challenging way to extend the activity. Ask children to select a 'meal' of ostinati, taking some food from the sheet perhaps and/or new ones they make up for themselves. Then ask them to chose suitable instruments – tuned and untuned percussion – on which to play them. Explain that they should combine ostinati to make the whole meal, chanting and playing and keeping a steady beat going throughout. This will be a challenge and is likely to need some experimentation and rehearsal.

154

The frog and the snake (1)

Make musical pictures to go with this story. Write and illustrate your own ending.

The frog leaped high and far towards the babbling stream.

In the stream, the water snake swam smoothly. Slowly it slithered to the shore.

When the snake saw the frog, it froze. It waited and waited, not moving a muscle.

The frog and the snake (2)

Cheerfully unaware of the danger, the frog bounced nearer and nearer.

Hidden at the edge of the babbling brook, the snake waited for its meal. Then…

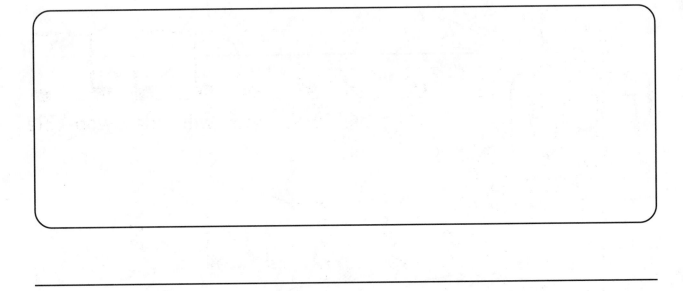

_____

_____

_____

Ostinati

A repeated pattern of music is called an **ostinato**.
These rhythm patterns fit the words beneath them.

 is a silent beat.

● Clap each ostinato six times. Hear the silent beat  in your head.

I - am - fed - up

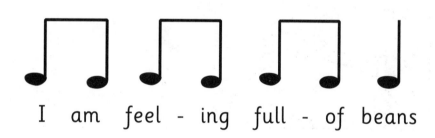

I am feel - ing full - of beans

wib - ble wob - ble wib - ble wob - ble

pease pud-ding hot

● Make up an ostinato of your own.

Food ostinati

● Clap these ostinati in your group. Half of you should clap the **pulse** and the other half should clap and chant the **ostinati**. Then swap roles. Start the pulse first.

Pulse: (repeat)

Rav - i - o - li and spa - ghe - tti

cheese   on   toast

cold mush - y peas

beef - burger cold

● Try out these ostinati using different percussion instruments.

RELIGIOUS EDUCATION

The teaching of RE in Year 3 is a statutory requirement and must be taught according to a locally agreed syllabus in all maintained schools, except those that are voluntary-aided and those of a religious character, where religion should be taught according to a trust deed or guidelines.

Agreed syllabuses tend to share common elements and QCA have felt confident enough to produce a scheme of work, even though there is no 'national' curriculum around which it might fit. Because religion is closely bound to strongly held beliefs, faith communities and cultural heritage, the syllabuses that emerge from QCA and local SACREs can sometimes sit uneasily with maturation levels of children. In their formulation, these syllabuses have to satisfy many demands, expectations and pressures.

QCA proposes five study units requiring 30 hours of teaching time. A locally agreed syllabus may not include the same or as many different faiths as are covered by the Year 3 QCA scheme and so could consume less time. The sheets in this book cover some of the same ground as the scheme. Some may not apply to you, or you may be able to amend those sheets that do not quite fit the needs of your school.

Where issues about a particular faith community are involved rather than more general information, advice is best sought from members of that community.

Signs and symbols (page 161)

Objective: To explore the difference between signs and symbols.

What to do: This sheet has a range of common signs and symbols that the children are likely to meet. Ask the children to examine the pictures and decide into which category they would place each one. This can be done by circling items in a particular category, by writing *sign* or *symbol* under each picture or by cutting out the pictures and arranging them in appropriate sets. Ask the children to think about what each sign and symbol stands for. There is a certain amount of crossover of meaning between the two words, but generally a sign has one clearly accessible meaning, whereas to understand a symbol you really need some wider knowledge. We would generally regard as a sign the male figure used to indicate the gents' toilet, but a good case could be made for it to be called a symbol. On the sheet, the cross, the dove of peace and the star are clearly symbols – the star, for example can have many meanings and contexts (on a telephone, an asterisk, a weather symbol for snow, often as a symbol simply for *cold*) – as they require interpretation

and other knowledge. The wash labels are symbols too, if not in quite the same category. The rest are more fitted to the sign category, although you might argue about some!

Differentiation: Some children should work in small groups to benefit from the support of other children. Reference material, such as the Highway Code and a garment with wash symbols on it, should be available.

Extension: Challenge children to find out about the dove and the olive branch. *Why does that image symbolise peace? What does the cross symbolise?* (You can also look at other symbols used in faiths that you may be studying.)

Objects and memories (page 162)

Objective: To examine how memories can be linked to particular objects.

What to do: Bring in an object that triggers good memories for you and share some of the memories with the class. Ask the children if there are objects that have a similar effect for them. Tell them to study the pictures on the sheet and to think about any memories that *one* of them brings back.

Differentiation: Talking about the pictures and memories is useful, so you could let some children work in small groups for discussion purposes. If writing is a problem, children could, after discussion, tell the stories of their memories to the class.

Extension: Ask children to bring in an object or picture and to talk to the class about the memories that it evokes.

Passover (page 163)

Objective: To learn the significance of Passover in Judaism.

What to do: This activity has to be set in the context of a study of Judaism, but it follows on work on symbolism covered in the previous activities. Passover (also called Pesach) recalls a significant part of Jewish history – the escape from slavery in Egypt around 3300 years ago. Tell the story. (See, for example, Michael Shire's *The Illuminated Haggadah*, Frances Lincoln.) Ask the children to imagine what it would be like if they were a long way from home and wanted to prepare a meal that would remind them of home. Then ask them to complete the sheet.

Differentiation: Some adult intervention may be required to help with reading if you have not been able to do much preparatory work. Books and resources for children to refer to should be displayed in the classroom.

Extension: Find out more about Passover and the Seder meal. If there are Jewish children in the class, ask them to talk about it if they are willing. The next activity is useful as follow-up.

The Passover meal (page 164)

Objective: To learn how symbolic food can be used to remember important events.

What to do: The children need to know the background to a Seder meal and Passover before undertaking this activity. The foods listed on the sheet are some of those in the Seder meal and they symbolise parts of the Passover story. Ask the children to judge which is the most likely part of the story that each one represents: bitter herbs – the misery of slavery; matzah – slaves eating only getting crumbs of food to live; eggs – new life, a new beginning after escaping from slavery; charoset – the mortar used by the slaves during the building they were forced to do by the Egyptians. (There is also plenty of information on the Internet, including www.judaism.about.com.)

Differentiation: Difficult new vocabulary will stump some children, so this will require some adult support. It would help if the new words are displayed in the classroom, with illustration if possible.

Extension: A member of the Jewish faith is the perfect person to explain about the Seder meal, so arrange a visitor if you can. Let the children try some matzah (also called matzos).

More than they say (page 165)

Objective: To understand how metaphors can convey religious meanings.

What to do: Before working on this activity, introduce the children to non-literal language. Talk through some examples of idioms like *It's raining cats and dogs* and *Daniel is driving me up the wall*. Ask the children to think about what these phrases mean *literally* compared to how we use them in everyday conversation. Encourage them to understand and use the term *metaphor*. In the examples from the Bible given on the sheet, the non-literal meanings may be less readily apparent to the children, so when the sheets have been completed, discuss the various answers presented. If you find it difficult to explain the Christian meanings behind these quotations, seek the advice of your co-ordinator. You may be able to involve a practising member of the faith community to explain and give background to the metaphors. (You could also try exploring sites such as www.culham.ac.uk or www.stapleford-centre.org.)

Differentiation: This is a difficult activity and some children will need to complete the sheet co-operatively and with adult support. It would help to provide plenty of visual material, reference books and so on.

Extension: Set more tasks that involve using metaphors and idioms. Ask children to use at least one metaphor in their next piece of free writing, for example: *He was a lion in the fight.*

Diwali cards (page 166)

Objective: To identify some elements of Diwali.

What to do: This activity assumes that the children are studying the Hindu religion and the celebration of Diwali. Diwali runs for five days, usually in October or November. One important theme is the story of Sita being rescued from Ravana, the demon king, by her husband Rama and the monkey god Hanuman. Another is reverence for Lakshmi, wife of Vishnu, who is said to visit every Hindu home once a year. An accessible source for stories is *Cradle Tales of Hinduism* if you can get hold of a copy. Try investigating www.hindunet.org/god and www.diwalimela.com. Ask the children to examine the illustrations on the cards on the sheet. What and who do they show? Then let them make their own Diwali greetings card. They could cut out and colour the pictures provided and include them as part of their design or use them as reference material for their own drawings.

Differentiation: Show examples of what the children should be aiming to produce, but this activity should be accessible to all children regardless of ability.

Extension: Use the experiences of children in your school and members of the Hindu community to explain about Diwali to the class.

Find out about the Bible (page 167)

Objective: To understand some basic information about the Bible and why it is important to Christians.

What to do: This is a straightforward cloze procedure. Make sure that the children understand that the missing words are given at the bottom of the sheet, and explain any references and unusual vocabulary where necessary.

Differentiation: Reading may be a problem as there is likely to be some unfamiliar vocabulary, so let children work in mixed-ability groups or pairs.

Extension: Have examples of different Bibles for children to compare. You could hold a quiz on basic facts about the Bible. Read stories together that the children might recognise, for example Noah and the flood, or the Nativity.

Signs and symbols

A **sign** has one clear meaning. A **symbol** can have many meanings that may not be clear and may mean different things to different people. Sort these into signs and symbols. Then write down what you think they mean.

Objects and memories

Objects can remind us of special occasions or good moments. Choose one of these pictures and write about the memories it brings back.

1.

2.

3.

4.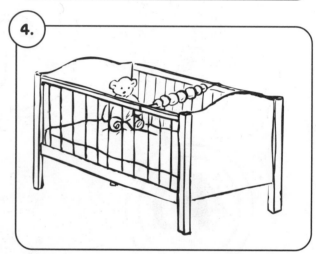

Picture [ ] reminds me of _____

_____

_____

_____

_____

_____

_____

Passover

Food can remind us of special events. During the eight days of Passover, Jewish families eat nothing that contains yeast. This is to remind them that when the Jewish people escaped from slavery in Egypt (about 3300 years ago), there was no time to wait for bread to rise. On the eve of Passover, Jews eat a Seder meal. Each of the foods in the meal is a symbol of the escape.

If you were making a meal to remind you of home, what food would it contain?

_____

_____

_____

_____

_____

The Passover meal

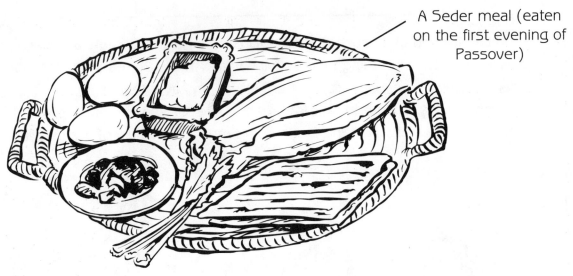

A Seder meal (eaten on the first evening of Passover)

Draw a line to match the food with the part of the story it symbolises.

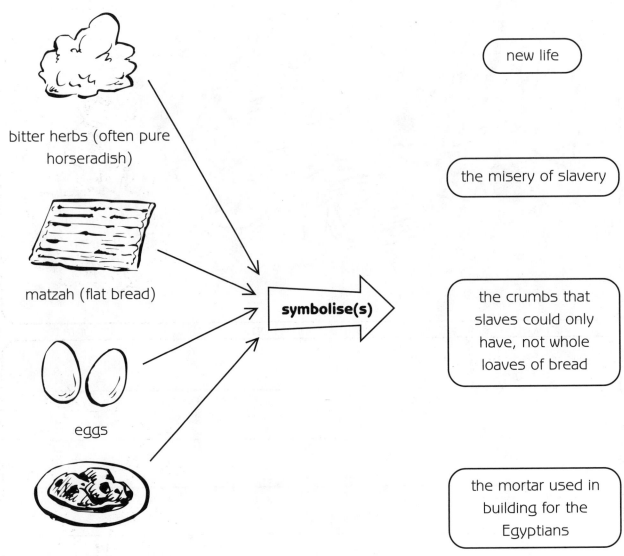

bitter herbs (often pure horseradish)

matzah (flat bread)

eggs

charoset (a paste of fruit and nuts mixed with wine)

symbolise(s)

new life

the misery of slavery

the crumbs that slaves could only have, not whole loaves of bread

the mortar used in building for the Egyptians

More than they say

Religious language is special. It is used to describe many things that are important and can be difficult to explain. Here are some metaphors from the Bible. Can you explain what they mean?

The truth will be your shield.

The Lord is my shepherd.

Jesus is the light of the world.

Diwali cards

Diwali is the Hindu festival of lights. Many Hindus send cards to wish people a happy Diwali. The cards often picture the gods important in the Diwali story.

● Design and make a Diwali card of your own. You could use one or more of these pictures on it.

● Find out more about Diwali.

Find out about the Bible

● Complete this passage using the words at the bottom of the page.

The Bible is a very special book to _____.

It is treated with great respect, so is called the

_____ Bible. The Bible is divided into two main

sections called Testaments. The first is the _____

Testament, the second is the _____ Testament.

The second Testament begins with the birth of

_____. The Bible is one book, but it is made up of

many smaller _____. People who follow this faith

learn how to be good Christians from the Bible. They read

it at home and especially in _____.

(books) (Holy) (church) (New) (Old) (Jesus) (Christians)

● Find out two more facts about the Bible.

PSHE AND CITIZENSHIP

PSHE and citizenship are not National Curriculum subjects at Key Stage 2 (citizenship is a statutory requirement at Key Stages 3 and 4), but schools are nevertheless expected to promote spiritual, moral, social and cultural development across the National Curriculum for all age groups. To this end, the government has provided non-statutory guidelines for PSHE and citizenship at Key Stages 1 and 2. This framework can be consulted in the National Curriculum handbook.

The children's knowledge, skills and understanding of this subject should be taught under the following headings: 'Developing confidence and responsibility and making the most of their abilities', 'Preparing to play an active role as citizens', 'Developing a healthy, safer lifestyle' and 'Developing good relationships and respecting the differences between people'. However, because of the non-statutory nature of this framework and the concomitant lack of content prescription, there are many ways of teaching to these headings. The Calouste Gulbenkian Foundation, for example, has produced what amounts to a scheme of work for the subject (*Passport: A Framework for Personal and Social Development*), but we can only scratch the surface here, for it is a vast subject that readily connects with others across the curriculum. We have tried to make sure that these photocopiable sheets can be used to support any approach to the subject that aims to work within the National Curriculum framework.

Saving for something special (page 170)

Objectives: To know why saving money is important; to understand about basic ways of saving money.

What to do: The child in the picture on the photocopiable sheet has one blank daydream bubble. Ask the children to draw in this bubble something that they would like to have and for which they would need to save up. They should then cut out the text boxes and arrange them in what they consider to be the most effective order. (D and E are clearly the best – for the

others it is really a matter of opinion.) The intention is that the various options should be debated as a group or class. Discuss, for example: *Why is it not a good idea to hide savings under the bed?*

Differentiation: This activity is made easier if it becomes a 'thinking aloud' task, so set up a group, with an adult leader if possible, for less able children to talk about the options given and to help them to make the choices.

Extension: What do the children do with their pocket money? Pose the question and ask them to prepare a pocket money budget that includes setting aside some of it as savings.

Jobs: likes and dislikes (1)

(page 171)

Objective: To know a range of jobs and work roles and what people might like or dislike about those jobs.

What to do: This activity and the variations on it in the following three sheets are intended to help increase children's understanding of how society works, so along with completing the sheet as a written exercise, there needs to be considerable discussion of the roles of these people (and others) in society. The best starting point for this discussion is to examine the roles of people that the children know. For example, talk about whether being a full-time mum (or dad) might be good or bad, and why. What is good and bad about being a headteacher? As you talk with the children, make a list of some useful key vocabulary, such as *proud, tired, interesting, dangerous, enjoy* and so on. It is not intended that every child will complete all of the sheets, although they would certainly benefit and need the balance from completing more than one. You could divide the class into groups, each one tackling a different occupation. Tell the children to imagine that they had the job illustrated on the sheet. What do they think it would involve? How would they feel about doing it every day?

Differentiation: Collect some reference material on the jobs illustrated and provide these as support for less able children.

Extension: Cover the illustration on one of the sheets before copying it, and ask children to insert a picture of someone they know. Then, instead of giving their own ideas of good and bad, ask them to interview the person and record his or her feelings. This could be done in school by prior arrangement with the people concerned, or it could make a reasonable homework activity if you have discussed a number of possible questions in advance.

Jobs: likes and dislikes (2)–(4)
(pages 172–4)

Objective: To know a range of jobs and work roles and what people might like or dislike about these jobs.

What to do: See the notes for 'Jobs: likes and dislikes (1)', above.

Differentiation/extension: These will be the same as 'Jobs: likes and dislikes (1)'.

Beating bullying (page 175)

Objective: To consider why it is wrong to bully and to start to think about strategies for dealing with bullying.

What to do: This subject is never as straightforward as it can sometimes seem, so tackling this activity must be done in the context of other work and discussion about the topic. Consider from the start questions such as: *What is bullying? How do we recognise it?* Ask the children to complete the sheet in pairs, then discuss their 'tips' for beating bullies. Lead the discussion in fruitful, rather than simply negative, directions. There will be school policies, county guidelines and other advisory material for you to refer to for additional advice.

Differentiation: You will need to be sensitive to the relationships within the class. Adult support is likely to be the key to differentiation here and you might find that you need to provide particular support to children who are being (or have been) bullied or bullies themselves, rather than on the basis of intellectual ability.

Extension: Collectively, make a poster list of class rules on how to deal with bullying in your class or school.

Looking after yourself
(page 176)

Objective: To be aware of health and hygiene issues and to accept responsibility for their personal cleanliness.

What to do: There are two different approaches to this activity. You could ask the children to complete the descriptions of their personal hygiene procedures first and then discuss them as a class, or have the discussion before the children go on to complete the sheet. If personal hygiene proves to be a sensitive issue for some children, you could tackle the activity in a more academic way, for example by asking: *What would be the perfect hygiene regime? Could you make up rules for teachers to follow?* The discussion should focus on why, how and by whom to emphasise that it is the children's own responsibility to care for themselves in this way.

Differentiation: Charts, posters, leaflets, books, videos and other reference material can be provided to support children who find this activity difficult.

Extension: This activity provides the perfect opportunity to involve health professionals, including the school nurse and dentist. Focus on one aspect of cleanliness in particular and produce a flow chart with the children, showing what should be done. Make sure that you ask, and the children ask themselves, *Why should I look after my body?* and *Who is responsible for keeping my body clean?*

PHOTOCOPIABLE

Saving for something special

To do or have some things, you need to save up your money.

What are the best ways to save money? Put these in order.

A. Keep putting it into your purse or wallet.

B. Hide it under your bed.

C. Give it to a friend to look after.

D. Put it in a bank account.

E. Put it in a savings account that earns interest.

F. Bury spare coins in the garden.

Jobs: likes and dislikes (1)

Imagine what it is like to go to work every day. You earn money, you meet people, but you must be there when you are supposed to and you have to work hard all day. You can't take a day off just when you like. Write down what you think this person might like and dislike about his job.

good → → bad

SCHOLASTIC **171**

Jobs: likes and dislikes (2)

Imagine what it is like to go to work every day. You earn money, you meet people, but you must be there when you are supposed to and you have to work hard all day. You can't take a day off just when you like. Write down what you think this person might like and dislike about her job.

Jobs: likes and dislikes (3)

Imagine what it is like to go to work every day. You earn money, you meet people, but you must be there when you are supposed to and you have to work hard all day. You can't take a day off just when you like. Write down what you think this person might like and dislike about her job.

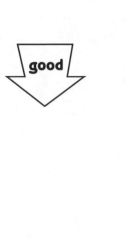

Jobs: likes and dislikes (4)

Imagine what it is like to go to work every day. You earn money, you meet people, but you must be there when you are supposed to and you have to work hard all day. You can't take a day off just when you like. Write down what you think this person might like and dislike about his job.

Builder

good

bad

Beating bullying

What if this happened to you? Work with a friend to write four tips for beating bullying.

No more bullying

 1.

 2.

3.

 4.

Looking after yourself

BODY SHOP

Only one body per person

How I look after my...	
teeth	
feet	
hands	
hair	
body	